"Wendland has made her r... come alive. . .you can almos... lingonberries at Christmastime and dance to the fiddle music of the Norwegian bachelor uncles. . .In addition she has paid tribute to generations of country school teachers—hardworking, dedicated and courageous."

—Glendale Herald, Milwaukee WI

"This book will enthrall and delight you as it tells about the adventures of Florence . . .during the pre-World War I era. . .and her tribulations with the Norwegian immigrants and their offspring while boarding with a variety of farm families. . .The easy-to-read style carries the reader along in a way that makes it hard to put the book down."

—KERKHOVEN BANNER
(A SWIFT COUNTY MN NEWSPAPER)

"Florence's five-year adventure is peppered with quaint escapades, including an encounter with rattlesnakes, a nine-hour misadventure in a prairie blizzard and her aunt Ida's wedding reception, when the 60 guests are snowbound overnight at Grandmother's farm.
With only one privy."

—Glenn Tornell, Director of the News
Bureau at Minnesota State University,
Moorhead MN

"The author has penned a work that combines the precision of a journal with the pace of a romance novel. Florence was one tough cookie who refused to accept the severe restrictions of her times."

—SANDI PAYNE REEVES
READING SPECIALIST WITH THE
GWINNETT COUNTY GA SCHOOL SYSTEM

"For me, Florence is a fascinating book. It brought back memories of different times, and a greater appreciation of those who committed their lives to the education of children."

"I enjoyed this book. . .the narrative is excellent. I could truly see the classrooms, homes Florence stayed in, and the people around her. She was certainly a strong woman and ahead of her times in her attitudes!"

"I read the book in two sittings! It was so intriguing and I couldn't wait to know what happened to Florence. The book is so unlike most biographies and reads like fiction. All the detail made us feel we were right there with Florence, almost living with her. The layout, the photos— all professionally carried out. Good job!"

"The book is charming, wonderful, heartfelt, and gives me incredible insight into what my mother's life must have been like, when she was a country schoolteacher in south-eastern North Dakota. Thanks for writing it!"

Florence

The True Story
of a Country Schoolteacher
in Minnesota and North Dakota

Audrey K. Wendland

Beaver's Pond Press, Inc.

ISBN 1-59298-063-5

Library of Congress Catalog Number: 2004103949
Printed in the United States of America

Second Edition: April 2004

08 07 06 05 04   5 4 3 2 1

Beaver's Pond Press, Inc.

7104 Ohms Lane, Suite 216
Edina, MN 55439
(952) 829-8818
www.beaverspondpress.com

To order, visit www.BookHouseFulfillment.com
or call 1-800-901-3480. Reseller discounts available.

For permission requests, contact:
Audrey K. Wendland
700 Bay Drive, #1013
Niceville, FL 32578

For more information on the book see:
www.awendland.com

Cover & Text Design 1st Edition: Dotti Albertine
2nd Edition Revisions to Design: Ronna Hammer
Cover Photo: Family Archive of Audrey K. Wendland

Dedication

This book is dedicated to the memory of my mother, Florence Thompson, and to all the other young teachers who labored to bring the three Rs—Reading, 'Riting and 'Rithmetic—to the rural school children across this great country of America back in the pre-World War I era.

This is her true story as she told it to me so many years ago. Some of the names have been changed to protect the guilty.

Author's Note: The Normal referred to in this story was established in 1885 by the legislature of the state of Minnesota, and graduated its first class of eight students in 1890. In 1921, the name was changed to Moorhead State Teachers College. After World War II, the name was changed again to Moorhead State University.

Acknowledgments

Many people helped with the production of this book. The most notable is my cousin, Verna Gomer of Benson, Minnesota, who spent countless hours hunting up newspaper clippings at the Benson Museum. Verna also filled me in on family background and historic detail. Doris Fischer of Rhame ND, another cousin, helped with the Bowman County background.

I love archivists! Korella Selzler was my first contact at Moorhead State University and Terry Shoptaugh followed up with more information from the Bulletins. Glenn Tornell of the Publicity Office, donated a copy of *The Moorhead Normal School*, a wonderful book on the history of the college. I owe much to Lois Anderson, superintendent of schools for both Bowman and Slope Counties in North Dakota. She sent information on District 29 and discovered more about the "lost year" of 1918-1919 at Scranton ND and Florence's top salary of $100 per month.

My late sister-in-law, Theone Kvam, was the first reader of the original version and gave much encouragement and help. Some writer friends read the manuscript and offered advice: Loretta Strehlow of Cedarburg WI; Mona Lawson of Jasper GA; Margie Kiser and Lou Krueger of Ft. Walton Beach FL among others.

Thanks go to my wonderful book designer, Dotti Albertine of Santa Monica, CA. Without her professional help, this book never would have come to fruition.

I want to thank all the friends and relatives who gave me such enthusiastic support over the years. I hope this effort will live up to their expectations.

Notable Quotes

"Persons admitted to the privilege of a normal school are expected to cheerfully comply with all the regulations published by the president for the guidance and direction of the students . . . and in general character, associations, and deportment to evince worthiness to become recognized teachers and examples for the youth."

—Bulletin of the State Normal School,
1903-1904; Moorhead, Minnesota

"The word *Normal* was used to denote a teacher school and copied in the 1830s from the French system of *école*—primary schools which were open to those who were to become teachers."

—Terry L. Shoptaugh, ACA Archivist,
Moorhead State University;
Moorhead, Minnesota.

Every man who opens up a road in the wilderness;

every engineer throwing a bridge over icy rivers for
weary travelers;
every builder rearing abodes of peace, happiness and
refinement for his generation;
every smith forging honest plates that hold great
ships in time of storm;
every patriot that redeems his land with blood;
every martyr forgotten and dying in his dungeon that
freedom might never perish;
every teacher who has gone forth to carry liberty,
intelligence, and religion to the ignorant,
still walks among men, working for society, and
is unconsciously immortal.

—NEWELL DWIGHT HILLIS
Dean of the Moorhead Normal, 1912

Contents

	Foreword	11
1	December – 1912	21
2	District 34	43
3	Ida's Christmas Program	63
4	Christmas at Grandmother's	79
5	The Year 1913	95
6	The Valentine Program	115
7	The Spring Creek School	135
8	The Holloway School	149
9	Ida's Wedding	171
10	Six Mile Grove: 1915-1916	193
11	Glimmers of Love	211
12	Bowman County, North Dakota	231
13	The Curran Place	253
14	Winter in North Dakota	273
15	Spring of 1917	281
16	Minneapolis in 1918	295
17	The Hendricks School	309
	Afterword	329
	References	335

Kvam Farm
1915

Foreword

Essentially, a historian does the same thing a historical novelist does—we wander about in the tombs . . . pure objectivity is a will-o'-the-wisp; chasing it is insanity.
— *Dead Certainties* by Simon Schama

When I was a little girl growing up in the 1930s, I loved to hear my mother's amusing and heart-wrenching tales about her life as a country schoolteacher back in the pre-World War I era; about the variety of families she lived with and the children she taught. The people of long ago seemed so heroic, struggling with obstacles unknown to me.

As a city child, I was accustomed to the amenities of urban life. A heavy snowfall wasn't a catastrophe in Minneapolis. The city sent out plows and the milkman continued to make his daily deliveries. We had electric lights and my father drove the latest model Chrysler. How different, and almost exotic, life had been for my mother isolated on someone's family farm.

Back in her day, travel was a hardship. The horses often couldn't make it through the snow and the dirt roads turned to mud in the spring. The country kids had to walk miles to school and they were lucky if they finished the Eighth Grade. People entertained themselves at home with the most simple of pleasures and if you could play the piano or the violin—that was the ticket to social success.

I often tried to visualize myself tucked away in a one-room schoolhouse, surrounded by corn and wheat fields, solely in charge of children ranging in age from six to sixteen; lighting a kerosene lamp or trudging through deep snow across a pasture. The rocky romance with my father intrigued me. These two young people had to overcome long separations, family opposition, hard times and a world war.

Money was scarce. That fact kept postponing the wedding. When my father finally felt he could support a wife, a simple ceremony was hastily arranged at the home of friends. People didn't have fancy weddings or honeymoons. Since married women were not allowed to teach, that ended my mother's bumpy career. She embraced her new role as a housewife and in a few years, her role as a full-time mother.

The years passed. I grew up, raised a family of my own and pursued my interest in writing. In the back of my mind, there always was the hope to write my mother's story. It took some convincing but at last, she agreed to help me make an outline. She was sixty-five by then and blessed with a remarkable memory. She could tell me the exact number of pupils in each school, the distances she had to walk and even some exact lines of dialogue. Amazingly, these facts fit with research I did later. However, circumstances intervened. I had to put the story away.

After her death in 1988, I felt more determined than ever to write this book. But where could I go for help? The story begins in Swift County, Minnesota, and I hadn't been there since I was a child. My best contact was a cousin who lived and breathed the family genealogy: Verna Gomer. She is the daughter of Ida Hanson, an important character in this story. Verna has lived her entire eighty-some years in Benson, a town of about 5,000 and the county seat.

So I was off to the land of my ancestors where I soaked up atmosphere, genealogy, and ethnic ties to Norway. We visited lichen-covered gravestones and restored country schoolhouses. Thank goodness for local historical societies! Later on, Verna sent newspaper clippings and photographs to my office here in Florida. I learned about the seeds of the women's movement, advances in medicine and education, and my own rich backdrop of Norwegian heritage.

The era became more real to me. I could see the apple orchard that lay between the Hanson farm and the District 88 schoolhouse. I could hear old H.R. Hanson himself, reading the Bible in Norwegian in his sing-song monotonous voice on Sunday evenings in the parlor. Florence's name leapt out at me as I studied lists of teachers in the various districts. These young women, fresh from the Normal with only a year or two of training, arrived and departed at a dizzying pace. The school terms were haphazard at best, devised not by state regulation but according to the needs of the local farmers. I often had to rely on my original outline.

The mists of history and the stirrings of the human heart can be difficult to penetrate but for me, one theme emerged from all this gathering of material. These were brave and heroic people who didn't look upon their lives as hardship. They made the best of whatever came along, just as their pioneer forefathers had done when they settled in Minnesota and North Dakota. Like the heroine of this story, they always were looking for a better day.

I hope you will enjoy reading about this headstrong girl named Florence who lived through it all, and was so determined to succeed.

Florence, on left, with her friends at the Normal School at Moorhead, Minnesota.

Florence

ADMISSION, ADVANCED STANDING, DIPLOMAS, AND CERTIFICATES

Registration Fee: The Registration Fee is one dollar and a half.

The Life Diploma: For admission to work leading to a life diploma the applicant must be:

(1) a graduate of an approved high school . . . or,

(2) present high school records, for which advanced credits will be given for a semester or more of work in a high school; or,

(3) sustain satisfactory examinations in each of the following subjects: arithmetic, English grammar, geography, U.S. History, and physiology, which test the applicant's knowledge of the subjects so named, as they are presented in the current leading textbooks. Applicants will be expected to show ability to read on sight, intelligently and fluently, ordinary, easy prose and simple poetry, and sufficient training in English composition to enable them to write a simple essay, or letter, correctly, and in proper form.

There are 60 units of work in the course of study. A minimum of one year's resident study is required of every candidate for graduation.

— The Bulletin of the State Normal School; Moorhead, Minnesota 1911

Author's note:

Florence completed one year of high school in Blair, Wisconsin, while boarding with her aunt Caroline. The town where her family was living at the time, Detroit Lakes, Minnesota, did not have a high school.

Tuition was free at the Normal if a student gave a solemn pledge to teach in the state of Minnesota for at least two years. However, room and board at Wheeler Hall came to $3.50 a week and Florence was broke. Grandfather Thompson came to the rescue with a little financial aid. After passing the entrance exams, Florence was able to complete eleven months of study before her money ran out. She received a Second Class Certificate, which enabled her to begin teaching at the age of seventeen.

The state of Minnesota was so desperate for teachers, the one-year residency requirement was waived in Florence's case.

Florence's class showing 6 students, Florence on far right

Florence

1915
RULES FOR TEACHERS

1. You may not marry during the term of your contract.

2. You are not to keep company with men.

3. You must be home between the hours of 8 p.m. and 6 a..m. unless attending a school function.

4. You may not loiter downtown in ice cream stores.

5. You may not travel beyond the city limits unless you have the permission of the chairman of the board.

6. You may not ride in a carriage or automobile with any man unless he is your father or brother.

7. You may not smoke cigarettes.

8. You may not dress in bright colors.

9. You may under no circumstances dye your hair.

10. You must wear at least two petticoats.

11. Your dresses must not be any shorter than two inches above the ankle.

12. To keep the school room neat and clean, you must: sweep the floor at least once daily; scrub the floor at least once a week with hot, soapy water; clean the blackboards at least once a day; and start the fire at 7 a.m. so the room will be warm by 8 a.m.

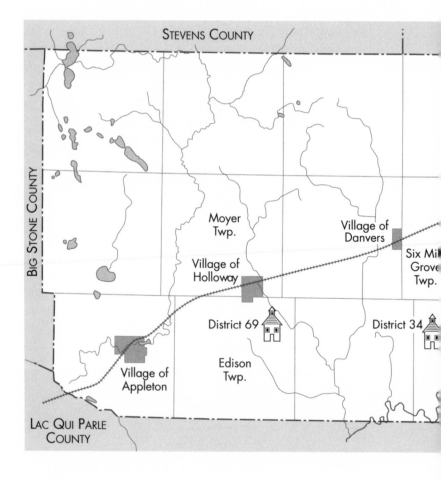

STEVENS COUNTY

BIG STONE COUNTY

Moyer Twp.

Village of Danvers

Six Mi[le] Grove Twp.

Village of Holloway

District 69

District 34

Edison Twp.

Village of Appleton

LAC QUI PARLE COUNTY

SWIFT COUNTY
MINNESOTA

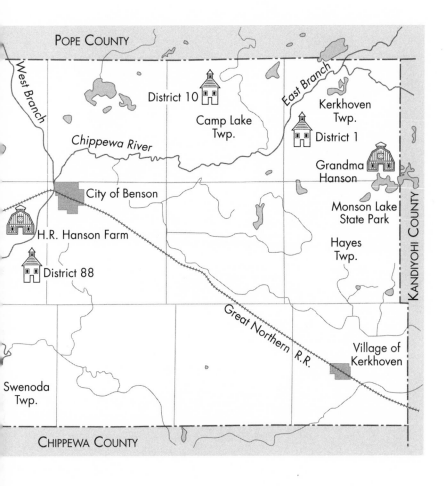

POPE COUNTY

West Branch

District 10

Camp Lake Twp.

East Branch

Chippewa River

Kerkhoven Twp.

District 1

Grandma Hanson

City of Benson

Monson Lake State Park

H.R. Hanson Farm

Hayes Twp.

District 88

KANDIYOHI COUNTY

Great Northern R.R.

Village of Kerkhoven

Swenoda Twp.

CHIPPEWA COUNTY

Florence dressed for class, about 1913

Chapter One

December 1912

The Winter Term at District 34
Swift County, Minnesota

"Oh, you dear little schoolhouse! I can't believe it, Ida. At last, I'm a real teacher!"

Florence Thompson whirled with joy in the deserted country schoolyard that Saturday afternoon, letting her long skirt swish against the tops of her high-button boots. The day was deliciously warm for early December, the tag end of Indian Summer days that had lingered longer than usual on the flatlands of central Minnesota.

"Humph! Dear little schoolhouse indeed." Ida Hanson folded her arms in a forbidding stance, spectacles sliding down her nose. "I never heard such talk. You will get so sick of that dump and those kids, you'll soon change your tune. There are times I'd give next month's pay to have a house in town, with a husband and kids of my own."

"You can't mean that, Ida. I always thought you loved teaching." Florence stopped her celebration to give her aunt a questioning look. Ida was her ideal of what a teacher should be. Yes, Ida was twenty-seven now and still not married and yes, Ida had been teaching in the rural schools of Swift County for eight years. She couldn't be expected to experience much of a thrill over the beginning of a new term.

"I don't intend to throw cold water on you, Florence. But you aren't exactly a success at this as yet. Just take a good look at that schoolhouse. The place looks worse than it did when I was teaching here five years ago."

Florence studied the squat frame building set on a crumbling stone foundation. The wooden steps up to the schoolhouse door looked rotted. The little cupola on the rooftop leaned at a slant and Florence doubted the bell up there would even work. Remnants of paint peeled from the buff-colored siding and from the privy that sat behind the schoolhouse. Two of the tall windows had been sealed over with thick butcher paper and over in the south corner of the schoolyard, behind the rusted swings, lurked a deep muddy hole that should have been filled in months before. Miss Thorson, the county superintendent, had warned her about the controversy that plagued District 34. The local farmers on the school board were tight as ticks about spending money for repairs.

"Doesn't look like much of a place to me," called Augaton Jorgenson from behind the wheel of his Model-T Ford. "Let's go."

Augaton, dressed in a cap with a visor and a long yellow coat designed for motoring on dusty roads, was a wasp of a man, thin as a spindle and thirty-five, an age that seemed incredibly old to Florence. He was the erstwhile suitor of Ida and only for her sake, had he agreed give the two women a ride to the schoolhouse for a first look-see. Now he had to deliver Florence and her trunk to her boarding place at the Knudson farm. Augaton sounded impatient to be off.

Ida hesitated, to look at her starry-eyed, seventeen-year-old niece with a new stir of compassion. "Florence, you need to remember the hardest thing about country teaching isn't the sorry condition of the schoolhouse. Or the kids who might act up and make your life miserable. It's the *country*. It's so lonely, living way out here miles from town. And to make matters worse, you have to live with that terrible Knudson family. I boarded with them for a winter term and I thought those four months would never end."

Florence let these words slide off like trickles of rainwater from a porch roof. "I'm used to living with older folks. Didn't I board with Aunt Caroline and her brood of kids? I thought *that* year would never end. But it did. If I could suffer through scrubbing floors and washing windows just to get through high school, I can get used to living in the country, too. It can't be that bad."

Scooping up her long skirt, Florence headed for the Ford. She couldn't allow herself to become discouraged before she even had started. In all her life, she never had wanted anything more than to become a teacher. She had worshipped her teachers and hoped to be exactly like them, just as kind and gracious and knowledgeable, fountains of wisdom and grace. She had treasured that goal and wouldn't let anyone, not even Ida, spoil it for her.

Augaton cranked up the Ford, forcing it to sputter to life. This was the first time Florence had gone for a ride in a new-fangled automobile, and that was a thrill in itself. The Model-T was such a wonder, with its glistening black fenders and narrow rubber tires, sturdy cloth top folded back like an open carriage, coach lamps to light the way at night, and the word "Ford" etched into the front grillwork so everyone would know what a marvelous machine it was. Augaton was a successful farmer, and had become the first person in Swift County to own a motorcar.

Ida took her place on the padded leather front seat next to Augaton and Florence climbed in back next to her trunk. She felt the car lurch forward to the ear-shattering roar of the engine and they were off in a cloud of dust, at the break-neck speed of twenty miles per hour. The farmhouse closest to the school, within walking distance, always was slated to be the boarding place whether the teacher wanted to board there or not. Florence knew it wouldn't take long to arrive.

"Looks like the Knudson place up ahead," shouted Augaton above the sound of the engine. He maneuvered the Ford from the dirt road into a narrow rutted lane that sliced through the pasture and led toward the house.

A tall, two-storied frame house loomed into view, surrounded by a cluster of outbuildings. The house had a traditional front porch with a spindled railing, an entrance rarely used by anyone unless the minister came to call. Augaton headed for the side porch that would open to the kitchen. The entire place had a weathered look, as if beaten down by too many winter storms, bare as a skeleton without a tree or a lilac bush in sight. Florence guessed one of the low-slung outbuildings must be a pig barn and another the hen house. The most dominant structure was the hay barn for the cows and horses, wide doors thrown open, with a narrow cow path leading out to the fenced-in pasture.

"Doesn't look like much to me," shouted Augaton as the Ford shivered to a stop, setting up a chorus of squawks from the chickens pecking at the bare ground. A huge dog about the size of a Doberman streaked from the barn, barking and snarling. The commotion was enough to wake the dead, Florence thought, but no one appeared at the kitchen door. "Where is everyone," she asked.

"I told you the Knudsons are a weird lot," Ida replied. "The worst I ever boarded with in all my years of teaching. I'm sure Lillie Thorson told them when to expect you."

Florence thought for a minute about the county superintendent and how efficient she was. "Why doesn't anyone come out, then?"

"These folks are plain unsociable. They act as if they don't understand a word of English. They expect you to speak Norwegian like everyone else around here. How that bachelor Carl ever got to be clerk of the school board is beyond me."

Florence drew in her breath. They would expect her to speak Norwegian? She knew that Swift County was populated by Norwegian immigrants and their descendants, immigrants who had forsaken their hardscrabble farms in Norway to make a new life in the new land. She felt proud of her hardy ancestors who had come to Minnesota way back in the mid-1800s but she, herself, was third generation and proud of it. She didn't know a word of Norwegian and had grown up without a trace of Scandinavian lilt in her voice. Her mother, Isabelle, the eldest daughter in the Hanson family, had seen to that. Isabelle had wanted her children to talk like Americans. She was nothing like her youngest sister, Ida, who took pride in being fluent in both languages.

The barking and squawking continued to raise a racket. Minutes passed. More minutes passed. Still no one opened the door. At the Normal, she had been told that most farm families felt honored to board the teacher and now this lack of hospitality began to make her feel uneasy.

"Let's go in," Augaton said. "I can't vait all day." Augaton had the abrupt, no-nonsense, Scandinavian way of expressing himself and now he walked around the car to lift out the shiny black trunk.

Then, with an eerie squeak, the kitchen door slowly opened. A slender woman peeked out. With a wave of her hand, she beckoned. Florence guessed this must be Minnie, the unmarried daughter, who was twenty-five. But Minnie looked much older, pale as a flour sack that had been left too long in the sun. Her brown hair formed a crown of braids on the top of her head and she wore a long gray apron over her plain muslin dress.

Florence picked up her valise packed with her most personal essentials, and followed Minnie into the high-ceilinged kitchen, into the odor of boiling potatoes and the smell of an iron sizzling on the coal stove. The range stood on black curved legs and had a cavern of an oven on one side, and six round burners covered with heavy black lids. The room was huge and square like most farm kitchens, with walls painted dingy beige, and a utilitarian hand pump next to the metal sink. In the center of the room was a big rectangular oak table piled high with stacks of sheets and napkins, and nearby stood an ironing board draped with a half-pressed tablecloth. Florence noticed a wizened old woman huddled in a far corner, seated in a wicker wheelchair and absorbed in knitting a long brown woolen scarf.

"Hello," Florence said bravely. "I'm the new teacher. Miss Thompson. You must be Mrs. Knudson."

Not missing a stitch, the old woman stared up at Florence with round, piercing eyes like those of an owl. Her thin face was etched with tiny wrinkles and her wispy white hair was drawn up tightly into a topknot. She pressed her lips together and didn't utter a word. Florence turned to the younger woman.

"And you must be Minnie. Miss Thorson has told me so much about you. During our interview this morning." Her voice trailed off as Minnie picked up the iron and gave a furious swipe to the tablecloth.

Suddenly, the kitchen door opened with a crash. Augaton walked in carrying the trunk, followed by Ida and a huge man dressed in work-stained bib overalls and heavy boots. His mere presence seemed to swallow up the room; his broad and muscular chest, enormous shoulders and upper arms looked as big as smoked hams. His chin was covered with mutton-chop whiskers and his dark eyes seemed to smolder with some long-hidden rage

Florence offered him a hesitant smile. "Hello. I'm Miss Thompson. The new teacher. You must be Carl Knudson."

The farmer narrowed his eyes to appraise the young woman who stood before him, noting her small stature, only five-feet-two, her neatly tailored jacket and long skirt, her dark curly hair that refused to stay in place, her lady-like demeanor—all in one dismissive glance.

Florence glanced at Ida, seeking reassurance. Ida said a few words in Norwegian to Minnie. With a sigh, Minnie placed the iron back on the stove and responded in Norwegian.

Ida, sturdy and reliable as ever, made the translation. "She's going to take you to your room now. Good luck.

Remember, we will pick you up at the schoolhouse on Friday afternoon. I'll think of something we can do over the weekend. I'm going to wait out in the car."

Florence felt her lips tremble. It wasn't good to show any emotion, to weep and embrace her aunt like a silly schoolgirl. She was a teacher now and she had to act like one, in command of herself in every situation. She turned to follow Minnie out of the kitchen with Augaton close behind, carrying the trunk. First they entered the dining room, an austere place with a bare wood floor and furnished with a polished oak table and eight straight-back chairs, and then into the vestibule adorned with faded red-rose wallpaper and a tall umbrella stand with an oval mirror. Next to it hung a long-necked telephone set into an oak plaque, with an earpiece hung on a hook.

Florence felt relieved to see there would be some connection to the outside world and hoped she would be allowed to use it. Minnie opened a wooden door in the vestibule, to reveal a tall narrow staircase with high wooden steps. Augaton groaned and heaved the trunk to one shoulder. Then he followed Minnie and Florence up the passage to the second floor. Florence's footsteps, made even louder by her pointy-toes boots, echoed on the bare floor although she tried to make as little noise as possible. They walked down the long hallway, where every bedroom door was closed as if the Knudsons wanted to shut out the world. Then finally, Minnie threw open another door at the end. "Here," she said in English. And disappeared.

Florence entered. The room looked as forbidding as Minnie, sparsely furnished, with bare rafters overhead and a plank floor. The iron bedstead was covered with a lumpy-looking crazy quilt made from a plethora of scraps held together with crude featherstitching. There was a washstand with a basin and pitcher, and a heavy bureau with an oak-framed mirror hung above. A kerosene lamp sat on a small table with one straight-back chair. Florence knew this barren room would be like an icebox, come winter.

"Doesn't look like much to me," said Augaton. He found a place for the trunk in one corner and started for the door.

"Augaton, thank you so much. Now you're sure you won't mind about picking me up on Friday? I'll be ready to go at four o'clock." Florence blinked back the beginnings of tears. It struck her that without the kindness of Augaton and the use of his Ford, she would be marooned in this dreadful place until heaven knew when.

"Ya. Sure." Augaton smiled a wisp of a smile. "I'll come get you."

"I'll see you on Friday, then. Please don't forget."

In the twink of an eye, Augaton was gone. The door closed with a hollow click. Florence could hear his footsteps on the wooden stairs and then the sputter of the Ford out in the side yard. The house settled into silence. For the first time in all her seventeen years, Florence found herself all alone.

Now, like a sudden awakening, she realized how much in her life she had taken for granted: the noisy clamor of her six brothers and sisters at home; their shabby little house in New London over in the neighboring county, a house filled with beautiful quilts and rugs on the floor; the easy walk to the general store whenever she wanted, to be dazzled by everything from yard goods to fresh meat sliced by the butcher to big glass jars of hard candy; the happy companionship of the girls at Wheeler Hall. Always, always, she had been surrounded by people. And now this. Alone. With no one to talk to, no one to depend upon but herself.

Two hours of emptiness stretched ahead. Then it would be suppertime with this sullen resentful family. Afterward, there would be a long evening with nothing to do. With all her heart, Florence wished it had been possible to arrive on Sunday instead of Saturday afternoon. But Miss Thorson had urged this early arrival so Florence could attend the Sunday Social to meet the members of the school board. This kind of social had become an annual event, since no one within memory ever had signed up for a second year at District 34. Florence closed her eyes remembering.

"Try to make a good impression on Helmer Togstaad," Miss Thorson had advised that very morning in her office. "He's the Chairman of the school board and let me warn you, he won't help anyone he doesn't like." Beneath her crown of faded blond hair, Thorson's pale face had wrinkled with worry.

"I know it's important to get along with the school board," Florence replied. She didn't need to be told that was the key to success in any district.

"But first," Miss Thorson had continued, "I must explain the politics of this school. District 34 is shaped like a capital L. Like this." She sketched an L on a piece of paper on her desk. At the point where the two legs of the

L met, Miss Thorson drew an ominous X. "Here is the schoolhouse."

Her pencil pointed to one end of the leg. "This is where Carl Knudson wants to build a new school. And on the opposite end, over here, is where Helmer Tagstaad wants to build a new school. These two men are stubborn as mules and this fight has been going on as long as I can remember. The result is that none of the board members will vote any money to fix up the schoolhouse they have. Such stingy men I never have seen. Not even in Swift County".

"Why don't they just divide into two school districts?" Florence asked.

"Costs too much." Miss Thorson's frown deepened. "They never vote a raise for the teacher, either. Forty-five dollars a month isn't much. Especially when you have to pay out twenty for room and board."

"I'll make a go of it," Florence said. She was too polite to mention she was almost penniless and that eleven months of college at the Moorhead Normal had wiped out her savings. When Ida had told her about the unexpected opening at a Swift County school, Florence hadn't wasted a moment about writing to Miss Thorson about the position.

The superintendent nervously fingered her opal brooch. "I want you to know the children at District 34 are very unruly. They have a terrible record for deportment. Miss Gallagher just up and quit after the fall term, after the time the children locked her in the privy. She said that was the last straw, and she'd never been so humiliated in all her life."

"I'm not afraid of unruly children. I can handle them."

The forty-year-old superintendent gave Florence a condescending look. "You are so young, my dear girl. You haven't had any experience. I see on your record that you haven't even done any practice teaching at the Normal. You've never seen children like these. They are downright mean."

"I don't believe any children are mean, Miss Thorson."

"You'll see. Soon enough. I just don't feel right about sending a young girl like you to a school like District 34. But there isn't any other teacher available with more experience."

Now, in her barren room at the Knudson house, Florence shook off the memory of that meeting with Miss Thorson. Florence didn't like to be fussed over and treated like a child. She'd been on her own since the age of thirteen, ever since her father had died of pneumonia. All the children who were old enough had gone to work. Her mother's only resource had been a government pension designed for poverty-stricken widows, in order to keep fatherless children out of the overflowing orphanages. Isabelle had taken in sewing to supplement that tiny amount but in spite of everything, Florence never had given up her dream of someday going to the Normal. Then, thanks to the generosity of Grandfather Thompson, she had been able to attend long enough to get her Second Class Certificate. Eleven months. Now she wasn't about to let a little matter of unruly children stand in the way of her success.

Florence unbuckled the heavy straps on her trunk and unlocked the lid. This trunk, inherited from her father, was nothing like the steamer trunks most of the girls had at Wheeler Hall. Florence's was more like a footlocker. To make it appear more feminine, she had wallpapered the underside of the lid in a lovely pattern of primroses. It made her think of Grandmother Betsy Hanson's garden and a place of peace and happiness, far from the tension of trying to get along with her embittered mother, and far from the sting of her willow whip. Florence shuddered at the memory of that tall earthenware jar in Isabelle's kitchen, where the switches were kept soaking in water and ready for instant use.

The poplin dresses came out first, to hang in the narrow closet, and then her collection of shirtwaists and skirts, which would be just the thing for school. She placed her woolen underwear in the bureau drawer and wondered how her sweet-tempered grandmother Betsy Hanson had managed to raise ten children without ever resorting to a willow whip. Ida, the second youngest, often had remarked about that. Grandmother was as different from moody Isabelle, as Isabelle was from the much-younger Ida.

Such strange families were both the Hansons and the Thompsons, adrift and fatherless but still tightly knit and clannish. Take Ida, for example. All the other Hanson girls had married young but Ida had chosen a different path, and always had seemed satisfied with her choice. Until today. Now, suddenly, Ida seemed to harbor some regrets. Was she really worried about becoming a spinster?

Such a thought was far from Florence's mind at age seventeen. She had years ahead of her to cope with the stupid law that forbade married women to teach. Perhaps women would get the vote before she reached Ida's age, and then that law would go straight to the garbage heap where it belonged. But she realized that laws did not change very quickly. Even President Woodrow Wilson, who seemed so smart about everything else, didn't think that women's suffrage was very important.

Florence closed her trunk and sat down to ponder Ida's most recent bit of advice. *Let your trunk be your castle. Not your boarding place or your school or your brightest student. It's better not to get too attached to anything. Remember, the time always comes when you have to say—goodbye.*

Goodbye! Florence laughed out loud. She couldn't imagine herself ever becoming attached to the Knudson family. As for the school and the pupils, well, she would need to wait and see about that.

On Sunday morning, a marvelous thing happened. Over a breakfast of pancakes and bacon, Florence noticed no preparations were being made to go to church. A boarding teacher was expected to attend services with the family, so this meant she would be spared from attending a long boring Lutheran service preached in the sort of "high" Norwegian the ministers learned in seminary. It appeared that Minnie and Carl were not church-goers like most of the God-fearing farmers.

Florence considered herself a good Christian and had studied her Luther's Catechism as a youngster but still, it had been a relief to stay in her room that morning and have the chance to take a warm sponge bath. Not speaking Norwegian, she didn't know how to ask for privacy in the kitchen, so she could heat water and take a bath in a proper tub. Now there would be plenty of time to get dressed for the Sunday Social that afternoon.

She decided on her second-best skirt of robin's egg blue and her very best white ruffled shirtwaist. Florence pinned up her unruly hair to make herself appear older, and used a bit of rice powder so her nose would not be shiny. She surveyed herself in the mirror and felt certain she would make a very good impression on the school board, and rehearsed the little talk she would give about plans for the winter term. She wanted to ask for lots of participation from the parents.

Carl hitched up the wagon about two o'clock that afternoon and escorted her to the Togstaad social just a few miles away. Florence felt surprised to see so many wagons and buggies in the front yard and when she walked into the parlor, she found a crowd of about forty men, women and children. The entire school district had turned out to greet her!

She paused near the doorway and waited for someone to step forward to introduce her. The room was abuzz with chattering voices but Florence could catch only an occasional word. Then slowly, she realized all these people were speaking a kind of "kitchen" Norwegian sprinkled with a few words of English. It was the odd mix-mosh the descendants of immigrants used.

Carl had headed for the buffet table in the dining room

and finally, tired of waiting for something to happen, Florence introduced herself to a small, dark-haired woman of about thirty who seemed to have an air of importance, bustling from parlor to dining room to kitchen, re-filling platters of food. "Hello. I'm Miss Thompson. The new teacher."

"Ja! Hvordan stär det til?"

"Sorry. I speak only English."

"Ja!" The lady gave Florence a startled look and taking the young teacher by the hand, she headed for the table laden with sliced blood-sausage and tongue, various kinds of cheese, crusty home-baked bread and an array of fancy Norwegian cookies that Florence recognized from visiting at her grandmother's house. Some of the people held small glasses filled with a red liquid. Since the children were drinking it too, she assumed it must be cranberry or possibly raspberry juice.

Florence had no idea what to do next. There hadn't been any courses at the Normal on how to deal with a school district that didn't speak English. Then a tall, blond-haired man strolled over in her direction, a man in his thirties with a trim moustache that set him quite apart from the other rough-featured farmers, who sported mutton-chops and chin whiskers. He wore an ill-fitting, gray sack suit with wide lapels and a stiffly starched shirt adorned with an embroidered vest with a watch pocket with a narrow gold chain. This was an indication the school board chairman was more prosperous than most of his neighbors.

"Vaersågod. Welcome. You must be the new teacher. I am Helmer Togstaad, your host. Would you like to try this drink? It's very good." His voice ranged up and down the scale in the Norwegian sing-song way and his engaging smile put her momentarily at ease.

Pleased to get some attention at last, Florence accepted the little glass he offered. She took a tentative sip. The juice seared her tongue like a hot flame and burned its way down her throat. She choked back a cough and felt her cheeks turning bright red as the drink.

A sly grin crept over Togstaad's face. "The new teachers never seem to like my chokecherry wine. I make it myself." Then he studied her in an appraising way—taking in her petite stature, her fresh, schoolgirl face. "Vy, you don't even look fifteen."

"Fifteen! I'm seventeen and you know that very well. You hired me." Florence tried to stuff back her rising sense of outrage. First she had been ignored, then stared at as if she were a prize heifer on display, then given this awful drink without any warning about how strong it was. And now she was being ridiculed in front of everyone.

Togstaad laughed. "So I did. Hire you. Ven Miss Thorson said there was no one else available. I yust didn't expect such a little girl. A headstrong girl at that, to speak up in such a vay." He nodded in the direction of the dark-haired woman and his voice softened a little. "You have met my sister, Kari. She comes in to cook and clean for me, and help with my son, Erik. He is in First Grade. I lost my wife last year. Pneumonia. It's been very hard on Erik. Come. Meet the school board."

Florence felt herself being pulled through the crowd, over toward a circle of men who seemed to be engaged in a loud, ill-tempered discussion.

"Gentlemen, this is the new teacher. Miss Thompson, meet Mr. Hagen, Mr. Christensen and Mr. Rodahl."

Each man stretched out a hand to shake hers in the hearty Norwegian way, up and down like the handle on a pump. Then they rolled their eyes at one another, apparently surprised to meet someone who looked so young.

"Now you will meet the wives," Togstaad announced, and took her to meet the circle of women, all with unpronounceable names like Gjertrud or Ragnhild, with faces windswept as the prairie, wearing plain, unadorned, floor length dresses that were years behind the latest fashions.

After those introductions, Florence pulled Togstaad aside with a hurried whisper. "I wanted to speak to the group as a whole. I wanted to tell them about my plans for the winter term. I didn't know hardly anyone could speak English."

"They can. Ven they want to." Helmer Togstaad smiled as if he had let her in on a little secret. "Come, have something to eat. You look like you could use a little meat on your bones." He led the way to the dining table, picked up a plate and heaped it with slices of blood sausage and bread and a few of the fluted cookies. "Eat," he commanded and strolled back to the circle of board members, a circle that now included his rival, Carl Knudson.

The Social dragged on. The children of various ages, dressed in knickers or long-waisted dresses, stared at Florence as she eyed the blood sausage, uncertain if she could bring herself to take a bite. None of the children came close enough to say a word. At last, Carl Knudson separated himself from the school board members and beckoned to Florence.

"Time to go," he announced in English. Then he pumped the hand of Helmer Togstaad and said, "Takk fer matten." (Thank you for the food.)

Feeling a surge of relief, Florence walked over to the host who stood near the parlor door. "Thank you for a lovely afternoon. I'd like to come over to talk with you very soon. There are two broken windows at the school. They need to be repaired before winter comes."

"Ja. The vindows. Ve yust had a meeting about that. Ve voted to buy some vood and board them up."

"Board up the windows! But that would make the classroom so dark. The sunshine is our only light. Why can't you buy some new window glass?"

"The reason is *money*, Miss Thompson." He bowed stiffly, as if that settled the matter. "Goodbye."

A few minutes later, Florence climbed up on the wagon bench next to Carl. He flicked a whip over the heads of the horses and as they began the journey home, Florence attempted to sort through the events of a disastrous afternoon. It had been a shock to discover the parents spoke nothing but Norwegian. She knew certain areas of Minnesota still clung to the old ways and the old country language, but she seemed to have landed in the most cloistered and backward township of all. And then, somehow, she had managed to antagonize the one person she had wanted to impress. Helmer Togstaad.

She longed to talk this over with Ida who would be sure to give her some guidance and direction. But there was only Carl sitting beside her, silent as an ox. In desperation, she decided to make one more attempt to draw him into a conversation.

"Well, Carl, what did you think of the meeting with the school board. I felt very disappointed about the windows. Isn't there some way to change their minds?"

"No," he snapped. "It's all decided." Carl flipped his buggy whip again and stared straight ahead, as if fascinated by the twitching of the horses' tails. The wagon continued down the lane and out to the dirt county road. The only sound was the clip-clop of the hooves and the squeak of wagon wheels. The late afternoon sun was about to drop below the horizon, spreading oranges and purples over flat lands dotted with an occasional house and barn, over the sprawling farms with boundaries marked by a line of trees, over mile upon mile of emptiness.

Florence felt desolate. Perhaps her mother had been right, after all; that a girl shouldn't flounce off to college to ruin herself with books and fancy ideas; or think she was better than anyone else; or more enlightened than other folks about manners and deportment; that Florence should set about finding a good husband and forget about spending her money from Grandfather on board and room at the Normal.

Later that evening Florence lay in bed unable to sleep, unable to stop the tears sliding down her cheeks. She pushed off the covers and padded over to the bedroom window. By the thin slit of the December moon, she could see the barren farmyard below, remote and isolated. Was this the reality of country life? What had happened to her dream? Where had it gone?

Florence thought back to the glorious speeches she had heard at convocations at Moorhead Normal — about her advantage in being there at all, how she'd had the opportunity to soak up this atmosphere of scholarly inspiration; how it was the duty of gifted people like herself to carry the light of knowledge to the ignorant; to share all she had learned with the less fortunate. She thought about Dean Hillis who had warned there would be times to try any teacher's soul, a resounding message on the day he had awarded Second Class Certificates to the twenty young people in her class. From his place at the podium, his pince-nez glasses bobbing on his nose, the Dean had challenged the budding teachers to hold onto their dreams. Come what may.

Florence mulled that over. The Dean knew about the problems in Minnesota and the rapid turnover of teachers, how these young men and women fresh out of the Normal were expected to cope with the less fortunate who didn't want to be enlightened, young teachers who had to deal with school boards wracked with dissension. But she would never turn tail and run like Miss Gallagher, no matter what. There had to be better days to come.

Feeling strengthened now in her resolve, Florence crept back to bed and pulled up the covers. There would be no more tears. Tomorrow was the day she had looked forward to all her life. Her first day as a teacher. This was her chance to show everyone, including Helmer Togstaad, she was much more than just a headstrong little girl straight out of the Normal.

Lillie Thorson

Chapter Two

District 34

Florence awoke with a start on Monday morning. It was seven a.m. and time to get ready for school! First she had to use the chamber pot and that would require dumping the contents later outdoors in the privy. Then she chose her outfit with care—a pair of bloomers, her cotton camisole and white shirtwaist, a pair of cotton stockings and the required two petticoats to go under the long gray flannel skirt. The rules for teacher were so particular about the petticoats when no one would know the difference if she put on only one.

Next she laced up her boots and added a short tailored jacket just in case the weather should turn cool. Florence tucked her package of alphabetized flash cards in her book pack, and went downstairs to wash her face and hands after making the necessary trip to the privy. With relief, she noticed that Carl was already in the barn doing chores and that he had left the big iron key to the schoolhouse on the table. Minnie dished up a plate of pancakes and slapped it down on the table, bristling with resentment. Florence managed to eat a few bites, although she was much too nervous about her first day at school to want or enjoy such a heavy breakfast.

Once outside, she found the gate in the wire fence, closed it behind her so Carl could never accuse her of carelessness, and started out across the pasture. The Indian Summer weather had lingered all weekend, crisp and warm. Florence took that as a good omen as she entered the schoolyard and marched up the wooden steps of the schoolhouse. She unlocked the door and stepped into the cloakroom, a long narrow room adorned with black hooks about child-height on the walls. One end of the cloakroom would be for the girls and the other for the boys. There were shelves below for overshoes in case of snow. After hanging up her jacket, Florence noticed a full pail of water left near the front door. She would need it to prime the pump outside in the schoolyard. This was a daily chore she could assign to one of the older boys, along with cleaning the blackboard.

With the pump in good order and the water pail refilled, Florence peeked into the little classroom, the place where she would reign over her seventeen pupils. The room seemed a bit dim, with the top parts of two double-hung windows covered with butcher paper. Light streamed in from the other windows but come winter, when the sky would be cloudy and overcast at times, this room would be dark and dreary.

The wooden desks were arranged in soldier-like fashion with the biggest in back and the smallest in front, benches pushed up on hinges, inkwells in place in the right-hand corners. The tops of the desks looked dirty and in need of a good scrubbing. The walls were painted a dismal beige, a color favored by most school boards, and a big picture of an American flag graced one corner of the room. Above the blackboard hung a long metal tube supported by metal hooks. This, she knew, would reveal a roll-down map of the United States.

The teacher's desk sat on a low platform in front of the blackboard, and was equipped with a long-handled bell to be used for maintaining order, and a booklet of instructions on how to keep the school clock properly wound each week. In the top drawer, Florence found the record book Miss Gallagher had left, and she quickly scanned the names. She noted a number of "F"s in the column for deportment and a sprinkling of "A"s in other subjects, mostly next to the names of Ralph and Alta Huston.

Florence walked to the back of the room to inspect the row of bookshelves. Pulling out an Eighth Grade History book, she examined the faded green cover and dog-eared pages. The book, she noted, had been published long ago, in 1905, and was sadly out of date. The McGuffy Readers had some pages missing and the arithmetic books were adorned with scribbles in the margins.

Now her attention turned to the round-bellied, black coal stove that dominated the back of the room. It stood on iron feet and above it was a round metal vent that reached almost to the ten-foot high ceiling. From there, the vent turned at a sharp angle to traverse the length of the classroom. This design was supposed to distribute the heat evenly through the classroom before being vented up the flue. But in actuality, the students closest to the stove were toasted into a sweat while the children in the corners would find their noses turning blue.

Florence found the broom in the cloakroom and swept the floor between the desks. Then she consulted the outline of lessons Miss Thorson had provided and wrote the page numbers to study on the blackboard. She wrote her name in school-teacherly cursive script and again in rounded print for the benefit of the beginning readers. Ida had said it would be hard to know on the first day, how well any of the students could read. It was up to the teacher to make adjustments as needed, to the daily curriculum.

By now, the hands on the school clock pointed to nine. A flutter of nervous excitement rose up from the pit of her stomach. Would this day be a success? Everything hinged on the impression she made on the first day. Picking up the school bell, the symbol of her authority, she walked outside to the schoolhouse steps. All seventeen children were gathered there, lunch pails in hand, looking at her with shy expectant eyes.

"Good morning, everyone," Florence said, feeling a new burst of confidence. "Please put your lunch pails in the cloakroom as usual. Then find a desk, with the beginning readers in the front of the room. We will make other seat assignments later."

With the smallest hubbub of whispering, the children shuffled into the classroom. The boys were dressed in knickers and the girls in pinafores and skirts that reached well below the knee. Several wore high-top shoes and some of the older boys had boots that laced up to the knee. They all looked neat and tidy, eager for the day to begin. Florence stepped up on the platform, rang the bell again, and pointed to her name on the blackboard.

"I am Miss Thompson, your new teacher. I'm sure we will have a very pleasant winter term. Now we will sing our opening song: *My Country 'Tis of Thee.*"

Florence picked up the pitch pipe she had brought along, to begin the mandatory anthem that opened every school day in Minnesota. A mood of silent expectation filled the room and then, before she could blow the first note, the cloakroom door opened with a loud crash. A tall, dark-haired boy lumbered in with a oafish smile on his face. He wore bib overalls and a work shirt and the kind of heavy shoes designed for work out in the fields. Under his nose, Florence could see the beginnings of a moustache. The boy looked to be at least eighteen.

All the heads in the classroom swiveled in the direction of this intruder and Florence almost dropped her pitch pipe. In her long recital of woes about District 34, Miss Thorson had not mentioned anything about enrolling a boy who was almost a grown man.

"Hello," Florence said, giving him a stern look. "What is your name?"

"Tom Clayton." The boy slouched against the back wall, arms folded, his gaze riveted on his scuffed and worn shoes.

"Please look at me when we talk, Tom. What grade are you in?"

"Eighth. Again. I missed the fall term and most of last year, too."

Florence knew it wasn't unusual to find a big, overgrown boy in a country school. The boys had to work on the farm and their attendance was spotty, at best. She decided to give him a chance and see what might develop.

"You may take a desk in the back of the room, Tom. And please don't be late to school again. Just now, we are going to open the day with a song."

Florence blew the note on the pitch pipe. She loved to sing and now she belted out the words in her strong contralto voice. The children chimed in and struggled all the way through the second verse.

"That's very good," she said. "And now we will say

the Pledge of Allegiance to the flag. Just pretend there *is* a flag and not just a picture of one."

She led the way, hand over her heart, and she could feel it beating in a quick, erratic rhythm. Could Tom Clayton be the culprit who had locked Miss Gallagher in the privy? But, no. He said he hadn't been in school the previous term. Could there be more than one troublemaker in the district? She thanked God she could go to the Knudson's for lunch. There would be no need for her to use the privy at school.

"Now the middle grades will study geography and the seventh and eighth grades will begin with history. The page numbers are on the board. Please pass to the back of the room and get your books."

All the older children scraped to their feet. Tom Clayton remained hunched in his seat, his long legs spread in the aisle. Florence knew she had the authority to ask him to leave then and there. She also knew she could call his father, if he caused any trouble. Fathers were very prompt about taking offenders on a trip to the woodshed, although Tom looked too big for this kind of punishment. However, she felt a little sorry for boys like Tom who didn't have much chance to get an education, so she decided to give him another opportunity. She walked over to his desk and said, "Get your book, Tom."

The boy slid off his bench and drawing himself up to his full height, he looked down on her minimal stature of five foot two with that same oafish smile on his face. The children stared and giggled. Then, apparently enjoying his moment in the spotlight, Tom raised his hand in a snappy salute. He turned and marched on stiff legs like a toy soldier to the bookshelf, and began an exaggerated search. He pulled out one book after another, ruffling through the pages. From under their eyebrows, the children watched. Ignoring him, Florence started to arrange a circle of small chairs for the beginning readers, and invited them to join her. Tom grew tired of his act and marched back to his seat, where he began a pretense of reading.

After the beginners were seated, Florence carried on as if Tom Clayton did not exist. She looked at the four little ones with a smile. "Now tell me your names," she said. One by one they introduced themselves: Ingeborg Tostenson, Selma Knudson, Lars Anderson and Erik Togstaad, the son of the school board chairman. Florence asked Selma if she was related to Minnie and Carl Knudson. She knew almost everyone in the district was related some way or another, by blood or by marriage.

The little girl screwed up her nose. "Yes," she admitted. "My aunt and uncle. We hardly ever see them except at threshing time."

Without further comment, Florence took out her flash cards and placed them on her lap. It was time to begin her first lesson in phonics. At the Normal, she had learned this new system of sounding out words and teaching the alphabet at the same time. It was far superior to the old way she had learned how to read by rote and with tiresome drills. Florence held up the first card—a simple drawing of an apple with the first letter big and bold, and the rest of the word spelled out in smaller print. "What's this?" she asked.

"Eple (Ayp-leh)" said Ingeborg in Norwegian. Her face lit up with success in making the right answer. She was a beautiful child with big blue eyes and yellow braids that hung down to her shoulders.

"This is an 'A' for apple," Florence said. "No Norwegian will be spoken in this school. It is nice to know Norwegian and speak it at home, if you like. But in school, it is good to speak English. Now everyone say the word with me—apple."

The beginners responded in an enthusiastic chorus. As the lesson progressed, Florence noticed that all the beginners could understand the most simple words in English. Teaching here would not be so hard, after all.

"How many would like me to read a story tomorrow, after we have learned more letters in the alphabet. I have a wonderful book at home called *Aesop's Fables*. It has many interesting stories."

All the hands shot up. "I'd like a story *every* day," Erik announced. "My papa never reads any stories to me at home."

"Then that's what we shall do," Florence said. "If you promise me one thing. That you will ask the meaning of a word you might not understand. And we can practice it a little."

The beginners agreed that was a good idea and the morning skimmed along. During arithmetic, Tom Clayton made a great show of getting a drink of water and rattled the dipper against the pail as much as possible. The rest of the morning he sat silent as a stone, leafing through pages in his book.

When it was time for geography and the study of the state capitals, Florence noticed that Ralph Huston kept hiding his face in his book, obviously hoping to not be called upon. "The others have all had a turn to recite, Ralph," she said. "Here's an easy one for you. Can you name the capital of the state of New York?"

Ralph peeked out from around his book and his pale face turned red. "Al—Albany," he whispered.

"Ralph knows all the state capitals," said Alta, his sister, with an impish smile. "He just doesn't like to recite in class. Ask him to name the capital of China," she teased. "I bet he doesn't know that one."

"We are studying the United States today, Alta. We'll get to China later. Now it's time for lunch, so everyone take your lunch pails outdoors. I'll be back in a little while."

Florence strolled across the pasture to the Knudson house and in the kitchen she found Minnie taking loaves of bread out of the oven and nothing laid on the table for a mid-day meal. The truth of her situation became abundantly clear. Minnie wanted a boarder about as much as Florence wanted to be there, and nothing could be done about it. The extra few dollars a month could not compensate for the burden of boarding the teacher. Now Florence could understand why Carl was so eager to build a schoolhouse someplace else, as far as possible from the Knudson farm.

"You don't need to bother about me," Florence said. "I can make a sandwich. A dill pickle would be nice. Did you put up any this year?"

Minnie heaved a sigh and crooking a finger at Florence, she led the way to the lean-to shed just off the kitchen and opened the pantry door. There were shelves from floor to ceiling, shelves crammed with Mason jars filled with produce from the garden of every description— peas, beans, corn, tomatoes, pickles—everything that could be raised in the state of Minnesota. Florence remembered how her mother hated canning season and the hours spent at the cook stove, sterilizing and preserving. A lump of compassion crept into her throat. For someone like Minnie, household drudgery would never end.

"Here," Minnie said, and thrust a jar of dill pickles into Florence's hand. Then she turned and wheeled her mother into the sitting room. Florence made the sandwich and the taste of the dill pickle was bitter in her mouth. It was a terrible fate to end up as the spinster sister of a farmer and on top of that, to be the caretaker of an invalid mother.

After taking a few more minutes to freshen up, Florence set off for school again. The first day was going remarkably well except for the unwanted presence of Tom Clayton. She felt he would soon tire of sitting in class with little children, and the problem would resolve itself. As she drew closer, she could hear the happy shouts of children at play and then to her surprise, she saw five or six of them running toward her across the pasture. Ralph and Alta were in the lead with Harriet Hagen right behind, the daughter of the school board treasurer, and the First Graders were trying to catch up.

"Miss Thompson! Miss Thompson!" the children called. For a moment, she relived her own school days, and how she used to run to meet her teacher, how exciting it had been to be the first to grab her hand. Today, Alta was the first and Florence gave her a warm hug. Surrounded by her pupils, all of them brimming with happy energy, she continued the journey to the schoolhouse. How could Miss Thorson ever have said these children were *mean*. Except for Tom Clayton, all of them were perfect angels.

As they entered the schoolyard, Florence saw Tom slumped on a bench near the swings, lunch pail at his feet, a morose expression on his face. He was the last one to climb the steps to the classroom.

On the dot of four o'clock, Florence asked for all the papers to be handed in for correction and rang the bell for dismissal. The day had been longer than she ever had thought a school day could be, but she summoned the energy to station herself at the door to bid each child good bye.

"Farvél," said Ingeborg in Norwegian. She giggled and placed her hand over her mouth. "Oops, I mean goodbye, Miss Thompson. I'll see you tomorrow." The others laughed and some squeezed her hand in a last goodbye. The children disappeared in every direction for the long walk home and Tom lumbered off toward a patch of woods. Florence hoped that would be the last she would see of him.

She stayed to prepare for the next day and it was almost dark when she headed for home, to climb the stairs and light her kerosene lamp. Florence was deep in thought, paging through her copy of *Aesop's Fables* to select the story for the next day, when suddenly, from directly beneath her feet, came a sharp rap, rap, rap. The sound was like someone knocking at the door but it came from under the floorboards. The room beneath was the sitting room where Mrs. Knudson usually pursued her knitting. Thinking perhaps something terrible had happened to the old woman, Florence dashed downstairs. There she found Minnie with a broom clutched in her hand, reaching up to pound the handle against the ceiling.

"What is it? What's happened?" Florence asked.

"Suppertime," Minnie announced. She gave Florence a surly stare, seized the back of the wheelchair and pushed the old lady and her knitting toward the kitchen. Florence followed to find Carl already seated, helping himself to a platter of boiled potatoes. Minnie snatched the platter from Carl and placed it in front of her mother, and then picked up a serving bowl of peas and carrots. Florence sat down and looked at the platter of sliced meat. Salt pork again. This was the same menu that had appeared on the Knudson table the night before, and the night before that; the same menu without a word being said in Norwegian or in English. Florence thought it was high time to break the ice.

"I've had the most exciting day at school," she said, picking up her napkin. "Your niece Selma shows a lot of promise."

Silence rolled in like layers of cotton batting, squeezing out every sound except the dull tick-tick of the clock on the shelf. Three pairs of eyes fastened on Florence, big round eyes that reminded her of owls perched in a tree. Florence took a bite of the salt pork and a tiny piece stuck in her throat. How could she endure dozens more silent meals like this, with people who saw life as a process to be suffered through, day by dreary day? She reached for a glass of water. She had four more months to go in the Knudson house. Silently, she thanked God there were only three more days until Friday.

On Tuesday, Tom Clayton arrived at school on time. He clumped to his desk and sat with arms folded, while Florence made her morning announcement.

"We need to make this classroom more bright and cheerful. We could start by scouring our desks. How many pupils could bring scrub brushes and pails and lye soap tomorrow?" Everyone except Tom raised a hand.

"We need to clean the walls and mop the floor, too," she continued. "I'm going to appoint a captain for each duty and we can figure out how long each project will take. That can count for arithmetic class today."

The children agreed with enthusiasm. The morning flew by as they made calculations on the number of pails and brushes needed, and then settled down for the regular lessons. After lunch, the entire class raced across the pasture to meet the teacher and grab her hand. All except Tom. Wednesday and Thursday sped by in a flurry of scrubbing and cleaning. The beginning readers expanded their vocabularies with *Aesop's Fables* but Ralph Huston continued to hide his face in his book all during geography and spelling. Nothing could induce him to recite. Tom Clayton continued to lurk in the back of the room, like a phantom shadow that would not go away.

Friday morning arrived. With her valise packed and sitting next to her desk for a wonderful weekend ahead, Florence sat in the circle of beginning readers, flash cards on her lap. The classroom looked clean and scrubbed, its only flaw the butcher paper plastered on the windows. Sooner or later, Florence promised herself, she would work up the courage to speak with Helmer Togstaad about that. She smiled at Ingeborg and held up a flash card—the one with a drawing of a bird.

Then, coming from a far, far distance, she heard the chug-chug of an automobile. The sound of a motor car approaching could mean only one thing—a visit from Lillie Thorson. The superintendent possessed the only other motorcar in Swift County, and it was much too early for Augaton. Miss Thorson was known for making surprise visits to check up on how things were going in her domain, and she was a severe critic indeed. The chug-chug came closer, growing louder and louder, and ended with a wheezing sputter out in the school-yard.

A heavy step sounded in the cloakroom. Erik Togstaad stumbled over the letter "G" for gate. The cloakroom door swung open. Florence felt her heart beat a little faster. Miss Thorson entered the room, pausing for just a moment to give Tom Clayton a stony glare. Then she settled herself on a chair in the back of the room, untied the scarf that held her huge hat in place, and turned her attention to the little circle of chairs.

Florence picked up another flash card. It was not in classroom etiquette to greet a prominent visitor like the superintendent. A teacher was supposed to carry on as if she wasn't there. Florence nodded at Ingeborg to respond, the brightest one in the group. Then, to her horror, Florence realized she had somehow, inadvertently, chosen the most difficult flash card of them all. The drawing of a spiky thistle. The "th" sound. This was the hardest sound for a Scandinavian child. There was no diphthong in the Norwegian language. Florence had planned to put the thistle card aside for a while, until the beginners felt more comfortable with the entire alphabet and all the sounds that were more familiar. But now the die was cast and not wanting to look flustered in front of Miss Thorson, Florence smiled and hoped for the best.

"Do you remember this word, Ingeborg? From yesterday?" Florence held her breath. She had gone through the entire stack with the beginners the day before, just for fun, but they hadn't worked on the difficult ones. From the corner of her eye, Florence saw Miss Thorson lean forward in her chair.

Ingeborg screwed up her face. Silence fell over the classroom. A few children dared to turn their heads, to peek in the direction of Miss Thorson. Another minute ticked by. Then shyly, Ingeborg whispered the word: "Thistle."

A surge of relief swept over Florence. "That's correct! Now can you say the word a little louder, so everyone can hear."

"Thistle," Ingeborg said. Her voice was strong with perfect pronunciation, as if she had been speaking English all her young life.

"That is excellent." Now Florence decided to play it a little safer, and produced the apple card for Erik and the bird card for Selma.

The superintendent cleared her throat and jerked her head toward the door, a clear signal that she wanted a private conference. Florence asked the First Graders to take their seats and hurried to comply.

"Where did you learn that method of teaching phonics?" Miss Thorson asked, once they were in the privacy of the cloakroom. "I must say, Miss Thompson, that nothing seems to be beyond you. Even though you are just a slip of a girl."

"I learned the flash card system at the Normal," Florence replied with a little burst of pride. Obviously, Miss Thorson had been very impressed.

"I wish you could demonstrate those flash cards at the Teachers' Institute, but it's over for the year. We usually hold it in the fall, before the weather turns cold. But next year, would you like to hold a demonstration for all the teachers in the county?"

"I'd love to, Miss Thorson. But next fall, I plan to be back at Moorhead. In fact, I want to start again in the summer session this June."

"Humph. That's what all the new young teachers say. They always want to go back to the Normal to finish up on their First Class Certificates. You talk just like all the rest. But then, once the teachers start cashing their checks instead of saving them, they change their tune." Miss Thorson tied on her hat with her scarf. "I must say this classroom never looked better. It's in apple pie order. Now tell me, how are the children behaving themselves?"

"Everything is fine. So far."

"Just wait. The roof will fall in on you when you least expect it. One favorite trick is to hide a garden snake in the lock of the schoolhouse door. So watch out for that one." She paused, with a glance in the direction of Tom. "If I were you, I'd expel that big boy in the back of the room. He looks like trouble. I know this school and the last thing you need is a big, overgrown boy to start a ruckus."

Miss Thorson paused with a knowing frown. Then she picked up her long yellow duster coat from a hook in the cloakroom, and walked outdoors to crank up her Ford.

Later that same Friday afternoon, after all the children had gone and the lesson plans were completed for Monday, the hands of the clock pointed to five. Where was Augaton? What could be keeping him? He was an hour late. All week long, she had been looking forward to Friday and seeing Ida again. There was so much to tell her, especially about the visit from Miss Thorson. Florence's ears strained for the sound of Augaton's Ford and now it was getting so dark, she had to light her lamp.

The thought of the weekend stuck at the Knudson house was more than Florence could bear. How could she spend an entire Saturday and Sunday cooped up in that drafty room with nothing to do? She paced up and down the aisle between the desks and then outdoors to look at the darkening sky. Another fifteen minutes passed. Tears stung her eyelids. Augaton must have forgotten his promise and there was no way to call and remind him. There wasn't a telephone in any schoolhouse in the county.

Sitting outdoors on the bench, she felt almost ready to give up when faintly, faintly, she heard the welcome chug-chug of an automobile. Her heart lifted. She looked down the road. The sound came closer and closer and the outlines of the Ford came into view. With the top down, she could see the two figures in the front seat, the coach lights on the front fenders beaming in the twilight. Ida and Augaton were coming to save her. Augaton had not forgotten.

Florence hurried back inside to grab her valise and jacket. She blew out the lamp and locked the schoolhouse door. At last the Ford pulled into the dirt driveway. "Augaton," she cried. "I was so afraid you weren't coming!"

"Land sakes, girl," Ida called from the front seat. "You didn't really think we would forget, did you? Augaton had to wait at my school until I could get my lesson plans finished for Monday."

Florence climbed into the back seat, letting all the relief and happiness wash over her. Two whole days of freedom from the Knudsons! "Where are we going?"

"The Quales invited us to come," Ida replied. "Alice and Ed. They're a young couple I know in my district. The best part is they don't have children. I don't have to feel like a schoolteacher when I'm at their place. They play whist. They dance. Alice and Ed are a lot of fun and I certainly could use some. It's been a hard week."

Ida's sing-song voice drifted over Florence like a melody. Whist—her favorite card game. And she loved to dance and be with young people who knew how to enjoy themselves. The Quale place sounded like heaven.

"I thought the people around here didn't approve of dancing," Florence shouted over the roar of the motor.

"Only the old fogies," Ida shouted back. "Like Carl Knudson. If Carl ever thought you went to a dance, he'd have a fit. But *some* people don't need to know everything." She gave her niece a sly wink.

Florence felt a shiver of apprehension. This neck of the woods seemed so rustic and backward after living at Moorhead, a college town that was up-to-date, where the students went to dances all the time. But should she put her teaching certificate in jeopardy, just to go to a dance?

What if some word about it drifted back to Carl? And yet, she realized times were changing. Sometimes they were changing so fast, it made her head spin. It was true she was expected to be a model of deportment and set a moral example, but did that have to mean never going to a dance? Never having any fun?

Ida didn't think so. During her years of teaching in Swift County, Ida had found a way around these barriers. If Ida thought dancing was all right—even in this pious, straight-laced community—then it must be so.

A little later, in the privacy of the guest room at the Quale house, Ida made a surprising announcement. "I've met someone really nice," she said. "He's the bookkeeper at the Olson Hardware store in Benson. I've known him for a while and now he seems to be very interested in me. Most people around here think he's a good catch. His name is Rudolph Johnson."

"Ida! How wonderful. I can't wait to meet him."

"You will. At my Christmas program. You're still planning to sing a solo, aren't you? I want to practice this weekend, since Ed and Alice have a piano."

"I wouldn't miss it. I'm sorry there isn't time to plan a Christmas program at my school. The children have been so wonderful and I hate to disappoint them."

"Those children? Have been wonderful? When I was at District 34, those kids were Holy Terrors. But that was a few years ago. Maybe things have changed."

"Have you ever heard of Tom Clayton?" Florence asked.

"Tom Clayton! Is he still in school? That boy is nothing but trouble. You'd better expel him."

"That's what Miss Thorson said but I don't know right now. I feel sorry for him. I wish I could win him over."

"Listen to me, Florence. You can't make a silk purse out of a sow's ear. District 34 is hard enough, without Tom Clayton around."

"The children have been fine. It's living at the Knudson house that is hard. They stare at me like a bunch of owls. They hate having me just as much as I hate being there. I'd give anything to board someplace else. But there isn't any other place."

"Let's talk about something more pleasant. I want you to meet Bert Johnson, Rudolph's brother, at my program. He's very good looking and a good dancer, too. Next to Rudolph, he's the best catch in Swift County."

Florence laughed. She couldn't imagine anyone being a "good catch" in Swift County. But then, she'd just arrived. Everyone couldn't be like the people she had met at that miserable Sunday social. There must some attractive bachelors around. Then she thought about poor Augaton. He had been trying so hard to win Ida's affection and now it appeared he was out of the running. Ida seemed very enthralled with Rudolph Johnson and Florence couldn't help but wonder about his brother, an available bachelor.

With a tingle of anticipation, she looked forward to meeting this potential suitor at Ida's Christmas program.

Chapter Three

Ida's Christmas Program

Florence dismissed class a little early, the following Thursday. She wanted plenty of time to take a bath in the big metal tub in the kitchen, and prepare for Ida's program that evening. Privacy always presented a problem at the Knudson's, so Florence stopped at the barn to warn Carl to stay out of the kitchen for an hour or so. Then she peeked into the sitting room where Minnie and her mother were occupied with rolling skeins of yarn into balls, to announce she would be taking a bath. She raced up the stairs and down again to start dipping water from the cistern. Every farmhouse had a cistern for collecting rainwater. This soft silky water was much preferred to the hard well water available at the kitchen sink.Using a kettle, she heated it on the stove while pondering what to wear that evening.

She didn't want to look like just another schoolmarm in a shirtwaist and skirt, while she was on stage singing her solo. But her other dresses, laboriously hand-made by her seamstress mother, looked a little too fussy for a school program. Isabelle made dresses for the fashionable ladies in town, but sometimes she got carried away with too many ruffles and an excess of lace.

Florence and Ida 1914

As she poured one kettle-full of hot water after another into the tub, Florence decided on one of her favorites, the light blue silk crepe with the set-in, wide silk waist band that emphasized her slim figure. It had a lacy over-skirt of fine cotton that came almost to the knee, a high-necked lacy bodice, and a separate long crepe underskirt that didn't quite reach the floor. The girls at school had thought it was quite elegant.

At last the tub was filled and the temperature just right. Florence draped her robe over a chair, picked up her treasured bar of lavender soap, and stepped in. It was such a luxury to take a real bath, a pleasure that didn't happen very often because the kitchen was such a center of activity. Sponge baths up in her room simply weren't the same.

Florence washed her hair and scrubbed her back, thinking how grand it would be to watch Ida conduct a school program. She was a true expert by now, and always put notices in the weekly newspapers, the *Swift County Monitor* and the *Benson Review*. The local farmers were so starved for entertainment, they could be counted on to attend almost anything that came along. The District 88 schoolhouse should be packed to the rafters. While lost in all these thoughts, Florence heard the heavy thud of boots outside on the kitchen porch.

"Just a minute, Carl," she called. "I'm almost finished." She popped out of the water, dried off in a hurry and put on her robe. "I'm decent now. You can come in."

Carl pushed his way into the warm kitchen, smelling like manure from the barn. "Where's Minnie?" he demanded. "It's almost time for supper."

"I'll get her in a minute." She hesitated, knowing Carl wouldn't be too pleased with her request. "I hope you haven't forgotten about taking me over to my aunt's school before supper. Over to District 88. Remember, I asked you at breakfast. I can find my own ride back after the program. It isn't far."

"*It's ten miles.*" Carl looked as if she had just asked him to take her to the moon.

"Please, Carl. I have to go. I'm part of the program. It will take me just a few minutes to get dressed."

"Vimmen," he scoffed. "All right, then. If I have to."

An hour and a half later, after a silent bumpy wagon ride to the neighboring township, Florence dashed into Ida's schoolhouse. This was the first time she had seen Ida's domain, considered to be the "plum" school of the county. Built around 1885, the schoolhouse had been kept up very well by a school board determined to give the local children a good education. This evening, a kerosene lamp lit every windowsill and a beautiful spruce tree stood in the corner of the classroom, decorated with strings of popcorn and cranberries and chains made of construction paper in red and green. The teacher's desk had been moved to one corner and Ida stood on the low platform dressed in a long gray muslin skirt and a ruffled shirtwaist, hair swept up in her usual pompadour.

"I'm glad you're early, Florence. You look lovely. I brought a lunch pail, so we can have a bite to eat before everyone gets here." Ida paused. "I feel a little nervous because we're going to do things a bit different tonight. We're going to have a minstrel show. Rudolph and Bert dreamed up the idea and I hope everyone will like it. The Hansons let me borrow their organ and Rudolph and Bert are carrying it over here." The H.R. Hanson farm, Ida's boarding place, was just a short distance away, an easy walk through the apple orchard.

"I'm sure everything will go just fine," Florence said, shrewd enough to realize it wasn't a mere Christmas program that was making Ida nervous. Her aunt might not have set her cap for Rudolph Johnson as yet, but it seemed likely she would. Ida was getting dangerously close to thirty.

"I can't wait for you to meet Bert Johnson," Ida continued. "He's a little younger than Rudolph, just the right age for you. He's so clever and all. He's bringing some burnt cork, for the boys to blacken their faces. He wrote all the jokes, too." Ida laid out the picnic supper on her desk. "Florence, it's important for you to meet a nice young man. They're not easy to find out here in the country."

Florence laughed. "I've been here only a couple of weeks, Ida. I haven't had the chance to meet anyone."

"Well, I've been here for years and years and take my word for it, these country bumpkins are scared stiff of a woman with a little education. Bert isn't like that. Or Rudolph either. They are modern men and they like to dance and have a good time. Rudolph is very talented and can play the fiddle."

Just as they finished their sliced chicken sandwiches and potato salad, the schoolhouse door swung open. Ida hurried to greet the two men who carried in a small brown pump organ. From her description of him, Florence guessed the bigger and older looking one must be Rudolph. But before Ida could introduce them, the families started to arrive, the women bringing huge jugs of coffee to keep hot on the coal stove and boxes of Christmas cookies. The room turned into a hubbub of activity, with children crowding into the desks, sitting three to a bench, while the adults sat in the bigger desks or on chairs lined up against the wall. The wagonloads of families kept on arriving, all trying to squeeze into the little classroom. Florence could almost taste the excitement. Soon it was time to begin and with a rustle of authority, Ida took her place on the platform.

"Welcome everyone, to the District 88 celebration of the Christmas season. First the children will sing a selection of carols, some new and some old carols from Norway. Please hold your applause until all the Christmas music is finished. Then we will see an original skit, the Swift County version of a minstrel show. These four young men will be in blackface and it's up to you to guess who they are. As the grand finale, Florence Thompson, the new teacher at District 34, will sing one of her favorite songs, *In the Dark, In the Dew*. Now children, we are ready to begin. Please pass to the front and take your places."

Ida helped the pupils arrange themselves in two rows on the platform near the organ. She settled herself on the bench, pumped on the foot pedals for a few moments and struck a chord. In unison, the youngsters sang a hearty rendition of *O Christmas Tree*. Next, the sweet voices lifted in a Norwegian Yuletide folk song, one that Florence never had heard before, a song that brought tears to the eyes of the immigrant parents as memories of their own childhoods drifted back, memories of the fjords and the deep valleys, memories of the brothers and sisters who had stayed behind, the relatives they never would see again.

During the singing, Florence noticed four young men slip in quietly from the cloakroom. They wore dark trousers and shirts with bright red ascots at their necks and white gloves. Their faces were darkened with burnt cork and circles of white greasepaint highlighted their eyes. Except for the leather strips of jingle bells they carried, they looked exactly like pictures Florence had seen of the real minstrel shows that were so popular now on the vaudeville stage.

The children finished with the last heart-tugging folk song and took their bows to hearty applause. Then the four minstrels stepped on stage. Florence held her breath, not knowing quite what to expect. Ida struck a bombastic chord on the organ to grab everyone's attention, and the act began.

One stocky minstrel stepped forward to ask in a loud voice: "Do you know what I found under my Christmas tree, Ole?" Florence was sure it was Rudolph under the disguise.

"What did you find Torvald?" asked the second minstrel rolling his eyes. This man was about six feet tall, the tallest in the group, and seemed to be having a lot of fun.

"A big bag of charcoal!" responded Rudolph the minstrel, shaking his two sets of jingle bells and looking very provoked.

"That's because you have the *blackest* heart," announced the second minstrel, shouting the words so everyone in the back could hear.

The minstrels kept complaining about the outrageous things they had found under their Christmas trees, complete with broad hammy gestures of surprise and punctuated with much shaking of the jingle bells. The audience loved it. Adults and children alike laughed and applauded. All through the performance, Florence kept her eyes on the tallest man, the one with the most grace and poise. He seemed to love being the center of attention.

The minstrels took their final bows. The little schoolhouse rocked with thunderous applause and the entertainers disappeared into the cloakroom. Then Ida stood up from the organ and announced Florence's song. She stepped up to the stage, nodded to Ida to begin the introduction and clasped her hands together about bosom-high, in the manner she had been taught at the Normal. She pronounced each word of the sweetly sentimental song, with diction so perfect it would have made her voice teacher proud. Time seemed to hang suspended as she let her glance sweep over the upturned faces.

She couldn't help but notice the tallest minstrel, still in blackface, standing near the cloakroom door. He looked enraptured, as if he never before had heard such a beautiful piece of music. When she hit the last note and Ida sounded the final chord, silence fell in a momentary hush. Then the tall minstrel shouted, "Bravo!" and brought his hands together in a loud clap of applause. The rest of the audience joined in a huge ovation. Florence could feel a blush steal over her face as she made a low curtsey.

When the room was quiet again, Ida thanked everyone for coming and invited all the parents and children and guests to stay for coffee and cookies. A few of the mothers and some of the younger farmers surrounded Florence, expressing their thanks for her song. They reached to pump her hand in the Norwegian way. "Ja. Very good. Ja," they said.

Ida pushed her way though the crowd to take Florence's arm, and steer her in the direction of the two Johnson men. "Come on, Florence. Here's your chance to meet Bert. I'm sure he'll be impressed with you." She tapped Bert on the shoulder. "Bert, I want you to meet Florence Thompson. My niece."

Bert turned around with a big smile. "Hello, I liked your song tonight. It was a dandy." He had been very quick about removing his makeup and now Florence could see his fair complexion and sandy-colored hair. "Sorry I have to leave so soon," he added. "Got to help Rudolph with the organ."

"It's nice to meet you," Florence said. "I thought your skit was very amusing." Before she knew it, Bert was gone and Ida had disappeared into a circle of parents and guests. Florence helped herself to some coffee and fifteen minutes passed, before Ida could thread her way back again.

"Well, how did you like him," Ida asked in her abrupt way.

"Like who?" Florence loved to tease Ida, who seemed to be an overly-zealous matchmaker.

"Like Bert Johnson," Ida said with impatience. "How did you like him?"

"All right, I guess. I only had about half a minute with him."

"Well, if you aren't hard to please. Here I go to all this trouble, so you can meet the most available bachelor in the whole county. And you don't know if you like him or not."

"Ida, if you want me to like someone so much, I'll show you someone. I like that tall fellow who was in the minstrel act. The one with the dark brown hair. Look, he's taken off his makeup now and he still has a little burnt cork on his cheek. He's standing over near the door, with a hat in his hand."

"Him! You like Leonard Kvam (pronounced Quam). You can't have any fun with him. Why, Leonard doesn't even know how to dance. What do you like about him?"

"I just like him."

"But—why? All Leonard does is read, read, read. I hear he doesn't even know how to milk a cow and he lives on a farm. His brother Orin, is one of my worst students. Leonard is just a stick in the mud."

"He doesn't look like a stick in the mud to me. And I like his city hat, too. Notice that it's felt and has a brim and a crown, like the young men in the cities wear. He doesn't have a cap with ear flaps, like you see around here."

Ida howled with laughter. "You are the limit, Florence. Ear flaps, indeed. Take my word for it. Forget about Leonard Kvam. Bert and Rudolph will be back in a few minutes and we will take you home in Rudoph's nice buggy. And not just a wagon." Ida poked a face at Florence in mock disgust and hurried off.

The crowd had begun to thin out a little and Florence cast another glance in the direction of Leonard Kvam. He caught her looking at him, and put his grey felt hat on his head in a jaunty way. Then he tipped the hat like a city gentleman, and smiled a radiant, entrancing smile.

"Goodnight, Miss Thompson," he called over the heads of the remaining guests. "I liked your song. I thought it was wonderful."

Florence felt a blush steal over her face. She watched Leonard leave with an older man who must be his father, and a boy who looked about twelve, who must be his brother, Orin. There was something special about Leonard Kvam. He had charm and wit. Anyone could see this man was definitely not a country bumpkin.

A little later, in the buggy chatting with Bert and Rudolph and Ida about the success of the program, Florence got to know Bert Johnson a little better. She could see why Ida thought he was such a good catch. He was bright and personable and good looking, a very nice young man who still lived on his family's farm. But Florence had met a different minstrel man that evening, one she felt just might capture her heart.

The next day, the last day before Christmas vacation, Florence sensed a peculiar tension in the air. All during the morning lessons, the children seemed to have their minds on something other than reading or arithmetic. The release from school for almost two weeks made her feel giddy with anticipation too. She was going to Grandmother Betsy's farm for the holiday and Uncle Bernt, Ida's brother, would pick her up at school. She felt so fortunate to have someplace to go, since her mother and the rest of the family had moved to Fargo, and she had no money for a train ticket.

Lunchtime arrived and Florence felt glad for the break. She strolled across the pasture, thinking the day thus far, had been a total loss. No one seemed able to concentrate. After the mid-day meal, Florence packed her valise and started back to school. About halfway there she paused, looking for the children who usually ran to greet her. No one came. She could hear shouts and laughter drifting over from the schoolyard but not one of the children looked her way. She felt a little apprehensive. Something was radically different from the normal routine and the ominous prediction of Miss Thorson came back like a haunting refrain: *The roof will fall in on you when you least expect it.*

Florence entered the schoolyard. Ingeborg didn't even look up from her game of hopscotch. Ralph Huston and a few of the other boys seemed absorbed in playing catch. Tom Clayton stood near the swings in his usual stance, face sullen, arms crossed. No one greeted her. Florence felt a tingle of apprehension as she went into the schoolhouse to get her bell, then ventured outside to ring it.

No one responded. The games continued as if she were invisible—Ralph with his ball, Ingeborg with her hopscotch, Selma on one of the swings. Florence went down the steps to call each child by name. "Selma, Ralph, Erik. It's time for class to begin."

Still no one responded. Florence took Ingeborg by the hand, then Erik, and pulled the children toward the schoolhouse door. Seeing this, Tom Clayton and some of the older boys began to throw stones against the wall of the schoolhouse. The girls joined in, throwing stones, clumps of dirt, whatever they could find, shouting, screaming. These children who had been so good, suddenly had turned into a sea of angry strangers.

"Here are some more stones," Tom yelled. "I've got a whole pile of them." He yanked at the swing, spilling Selma to the ground. Florence rushed to help the child and a stone sailed past her head. She grabbed Selma's hand and pulled her into the schoolhouse, and went back for the younger children. Once the beginning readers were safe inside, Florence went back for the older children, pulling them up the stairs and into the classroom.

Carrying a handful of stones, Tom Clayton went inside and pandemonium broke out. The older boys kicked at the walls and threw stones around the room. There was no way to stop this senseless rebellion and so Florence decided to simply let the scene play itself out. She took her place on the platform and waited. Five minutes ticked by in what seemed an eternity.

Then slowly, the outbreak lost some of its vigor. The children looked to Tom, as if waiting for orders from their captain. But Tom looked tired now of the whole thing and abruptly sat down at his desk. Seizing the moment, Florence rang her bell again and again until the room fell into a hush.

"All right. You've had your fun," she said. "Now stay quiet so I can tell you something very important."

All the eyes riveted on the teacher. Florence could feel her heart thud against her ribs. She drew a deep breath to calm herself, to wait for a moment of complete silence. Then she began to speak in a slow and authoritative tone.

"You have all been wonderful students. Yes. . .all of you. But the truth is, I just came here out of curiosity. I had heard such terrible stories about you. . .about all the terrible things you have done to other teachers. . .so terrible I couldn't believe what I was told. Now I know for myself about the way you act. Now I've seen it. . .and I have no intention of coming back here. Ever."

Florence paused. She saw some of the heads hang down in remorse. Some of the jaws dropped open.

"I feel very sorry for you children," she continued, "because from now on, you won't have a teacher. No one will want to come here, anymore. So of course, you won't have a school. It's going to be very lonesome for you this winter, without a school. And next winter will be even more lonesome. Without a school. . .with nothing to do. I imagine the school board will just tear down this old building. And that will be the end of District 34."

The closing of a school was not without precedent in the history of rural education. This was no idle threat. Other schools had closed because the children refused to behave. Now that she had the full attention of her pupils, Florence plunged on.

"I had so many plans for you. I was going to have spelling bees and contests. I used to love spelling bees, when I was in school. Since there wasn't time to plan a Christmas program, I had planned to talk with you about a Valentine program and that would have been lots of fun. But now I see you aren't interested in that. Now that I know how you feel about school, we can forget about programs and making Valentines."

Florence closed the record book on her desk, the symbol of the school year, and put it in the desk drawer with an air of finality. Seeing this, Ingeborg in the front row let out a long agonized wail. "Please don't leave, Miss Thompson."

A few lips began to tremble. Eyes began to fill with tears. "Please don't leave, Miss Thompson," cried Erik Togstaad.

Florence glanced around the classroom, taking in all

this remorse. The little ones were openly sobbing and the older students were trying to squeeze back their tears. "Do you really want me to stay?" she asked.

"Yes, yes," they shouted. Tom Clayton was the only silent one and he sat slouched in his desk, sullen as ever.

"Well, then. Let's take a vote. How many of you really want me to come back?"

All the hands shot up. Even Tom's hand was up, about halfway.

"All right," she continued. "But first, we have to make some promises. What is going to happen the next time I ring the school bell?"

"I'll come right in," called Alta Huston. Florence wrote the promise on the blackboard in her neat cursive handwriting.

"I promise to be quiet in class and never whisper," called Selma Knudson.

"I promise to fetch water without being asked," added Kermit Hagen, one of the bigger boys who had been assigned this task.

"I promise. . .I promise. . .I promise." Each student raised a hand with a promise and soon the blackboard was filled to capacity. Florence breathed a sigh of relief. Victory was hers. The only fly in this redeeming ointment was Tom Clayton. He sat silent as a stone, promising nothing.

Once again, Florence felt an urge to expel him. He obviously had been the ring-leader of this whole ugly affair but on the other hand, the children had been willing participants. It wasn't fair to make him the scapegoat. The whole class needed to learn about taking responsibility for their actions, and how to make amends. She decided to let

Tom stew in his own juice over Christmas vacation, thinking he probably wouldn't return to school anyway. She looked at the clock. Uncle Bernt would arrive soon and she had promised him to dismiss school early. They needed to get to Grandmother's before dark.

"Well, children. We've had quite a day. I'm going to leave all these promises on the blackboard, so we can review them when school starts again. Remember, if anything like this happens again, I will simply leave and not give you a second chance." She hesitated, to let the full meaning sink in. "Now you are dismissed and I wish each and every one of you a Merry Christmas. I will see you on Monday, right after New Year's Day."

Florence stationed herself at the door for a last farewell and in a few more minutes, the classroom was empty. Tom had slipped out, leaving his little arsenal of stones on his desk. Florence gathered them up and taking them outdoors, she pitched them one by one, into that bothersome mud hole out in the corner of the schoolyard.

And peace settled over District 34. For a while.

Chapter Four

Christmas at Grandmother's Farm

L ooks like we might have snow," Uncle Bernt said to Florence, looking at the ominous fluffy gray clouds overhead. "I guess the warm spell is about over."

"I don't mind snow," Florence said, climbing up to sit next to him on the tufted black leather seat. Bernt had brought his one-horse buggy and the top was down even though the weather was a bit nippy now. "It would be fun to drive back by sled."

"Young people," Bernt grunted as they started off down the road. "You haven't seen as many winters as I have."

This was most certainly true. Although Bernt was not yet forty, he seemed much older and set in his ways. He managed Grandmother Betsy's farm along with his brother, Julius. The two bachelors seemed slated to spend the rest of their lives on the land inherited from Florence's Great-Grandfather Hans Sagedalen, the patriarch of them all. Hans had packed up his wife and four children to emigrate in 1851 from Hallingdal, a valley west of Oslo, to seek his fortune in Minnesota. According to his emigration papers, Hans had been nothing more than a "husman" in Norway, a landless pauper. His choice had been

Isabelle on far left, Caroline next to her; Ida in white blouse;
Bernt and Julius on far right; Betsy seated in front.

Florence

June 1914. Hanson Family Reunion in front of farmhouse.

between starvation in the old country or the opportunity to find land in the boundless wild frontier of America.

The family had landed first in Quebec where another child was born, and then went by steamer across the Great Lakes to Milwaukee. From there, they had traveled by covered wagon to Rice County, Minnesota. This had turned out to be a disappointing choice. Too many immigrants from Hallingdal already had settled the land and Hans had to be content to work for others again.

After the Civil War, his son, Henry, had come home from the Union Army with stories of land available farther west. So Hans had packed up once again, to become one of the original pioneers in Swift County, before it officially became a county. Hans found some acreage on the shoreline of Monson Lake, where the Indians had been vanquished after the Sioux Uprising of 1862. Once peace was established, some of the original settlers had returned to the nearby little town of Sunburg. Hans and sons Henry and Tosten, each had staked out claims and that had been the beginning of a family enclave in Kerkhoven Township. Betsy, Tosten's widow, still lived there and carried on the old Norwegian traditions.

Florence had heard the family lore ever since she was a child but more important to her at this moment, was the prospect of a vacation at Grandmother's house. After a brief stop to pick up Ida at her boarding place, they began the long journey of thirty-five miles. Bernt listened in his stoic way, without a nod or comment, while Florence told Ida about the crisis at school and how the roof had fallen in on her, just the way Miss Thorson had predicted.

"You sure have gumption," Ida said after hearing the story. "You'd better expel that Tom Clayton before he starts any more trouble. Remember what I said about a sow's ear."

"I know. I suppose I should have done it today but I had hoped so much that he might change. Underneath all that nastiness, I think he's just a scared kid who realizes he doesn't have much of a future. He hardly knows how to read."

Florence looked at the boundless sky that seemed to beckon to an exciting world beyond the borders of Swift County. Tom Clayton seemed fated to spend the rest of his days on his family farm, trapped in an endless round of chores, and just suffocate there. How fortunate she had been in her seventeen years, to have traveled and lived so many places. She could recall the railroad town of Estevan, Saskatchewan where her father had been an engineer for the mines before his death, and the family's move back to Minnesota. There was no high school in her small town, so she had convinced her mother to let her go to Blair, Wisconsin, where she could board with Aunt Caroline and attend classes. Of course her stay at Moorhead and trips across the Red River to Fargo, were the biggest highlight of all. She felt almost like a world traveler compared with Tom.

"Humph," said Ida, breaking the spell. "I used to be as idealistic as you are, when I first started teaching school. Thinking I could bring education to everyone. I learned soon enough that doesn't pay. There are some kids who won't learn anything, no matter how hard you try to teach them. The best way is to expel the troublemakers and life will be easier for you. It's better for the smarter kids too, not to have so much distraction."

Florence mulled that over, as she watched the fence

posts slowly pass by. Perhaps Ida was right. She usually was. Florence decided to change the subject.

"Tell me about Leonard Kvam," Florence said. "You know the family so well. He seems like such a nice gentleman."

"Gentleman!" Ida hooted. "He'll never amount to anything and doesn't even appreciate the nice farm he will inherit someday, when his father decides to retire. Now Lars is a good man and I'm not saying he isn't. He's been on the school board for District 88 for as long as I can remember. But those two boys of his are spoiled to death. I doubt if Orin will ever finish the Eighth Grade at the rate he's going. Now Leonard is just the opposite. He'd rather go to school than work on the farm. This past year he's been at Willmar, going to boarding school, and wasting his father's money. I just wonder whatever is going to happen to this new generation."

"What do you mean, wasting money? Why shouldn't Leonard go on past the Eighth Grade, if he can?"

"Because nothing will come of it. Lars can't afford to send him to college to be a lawyer or a doctor. So what earthly good is a boarding school? The oldest son to supposed to carry on at the family farm. Everyone knows that."

Once again, Florence realized that Ida probably was right. There weren't many avenues open to anyone these days, not even to men, to better themselves. And yet, Florence felt that Leonard must know what he was doing. Not everyone in this world was cut out to be a farmer.

It was almost dark when the carriage arrived at Grandmother's. This was the spacious Victorian frame house that Florence remembered as a child. She always had felt awed by the size of this place. It had fifteen rooms, with the customary front porch decorated with tall pillars and wood carvings in the corners. Sturdy metal gutters slanted down from the high pitched roof and came together in a V shape, to catch rainwater for the cistern. She remembered exploring the sod hut that Grandfather Tosten had built for his bride way back in 1868. The little shanty still stood near the house, like a reminder of past struggles. Although she couldn't remember him very well, Florence had heard the stories about Tosten and how strong he was; how he had walked to St. Cloud for supplies seventy miles away, because at the beginning he couldn't even afford a horse and wagon.

The family had prospered. Tosten's wife Berit, from Valdres, Norway, changed her name to Betsy, taking a cue from other immigrants who wanted to be Americans. They no longer wanted to be called Berit or Gunhild or Gjertrud. They wanted to be Betsy or Julia or Sophia. Ten children were born and eight of them had survived. Her grandparents had been very fortunate until Tosten's unexpected death in 1908. And now, with most of the children married and gone, Betsy still lived on the farm with the help of Bernt and Julius.

Grabbing her valise, Florence jumped out of the carriage and ran into the kitchen, where she found Betsy baking bread. "Grandmother, I'm so happy to be here. Thank you so much for asking me."

"Child, how you have grown," exclaimed Betsy, wiping flour from her hands. She was a slender and work-worn woman, still the center of her ever-increasing family of grandchildren, jolly and full of life at age sixty-five. Her gray hair was pulled up in a topknot and she wore a long immaculate apron over her floor-length brown skirt.

"Now tell me you haven't finished all the baking," Florence said. "I'm not very good at cooking but I want to help."

Betsy smiled. "I saved some jobs for you. There are the lingonberries to clean. And the lefse to bake. I've been waiting for you and Ida to decorate the tree."

The general store at Sunburg, the nearest town, imported lingonberries by the barrel from the old country, not only for Christmas but year-round. The tiny bright-red berries had a slightly tart flavor, delicious with chicken or pork. Florence knew that lefse (LEF-sa) required russet potatoes and the sure knowledge of how much flour and water to add, to turn out the soft potato flat bread that was more like an extra-thin, round pancake. The old-timers never used recipes. There was a trick to lifting a piece from the griddle with a long, carefully whittled lefse stick. This had to be done just once, at the vital moment, to turn it. Lefse was so filling it had been peasant food back in Norway but now, the potato flat bread was considered a holiday treat. Even Isabelle, who followed very few Norwegian traditions, always baked lefse for Christmas.

It took no time at all for Florence and Ida to settle into Ida's old room. A chill hung in the air in the upper reaches of the house, but there was plenty of warmth in the huge kitchen, the place that was the heart of the family.

After a light supper of home-made cheese and sausage, together with Betsy's crusty white bread, they sat around the kitchen table laughing and telling stories of the olden days. Uncle Julius was like a younger edition of Bernt, tall, handsome and shy, and just as set in his ways. Bernt was just about to deal a hand of whist when suddenly, a sharp rap pounded on the kitchen door. Florence could hear peals of laughter and the unmistakable sound of jingling sleigh bells.

"It's the Jule Bukk (YOU-la-bok)" shrieked Grandmother in delight.* Florence looked at Ida in confusion. This was something she never had heard of before.

"Jule Bukk means Christmas Fools," Ida explained, looking a little mortified by her mother's enthusiastic reaction. "You'll see what the game is all about in a minute."

With a whoop and a shout, three queer-looking people, two men and a woman, burst into the toasty kitchen. Tightly fitted knit ski caps covered their faces with holes for their eyes and mouths. Red and white striped long shirts hung from their shoulders and the two men wore leggings with jingle bells tied to their knees. The woman wore a long skirt and shook the leather strips of bells in her hands, like castanets. "God Yul," they cried in a chorus. (Good Christmas).

"Now we're supposed to guess who they are," Ida said,

---

*"Christmas Fool" is the Swift County translation. In Norway, the expression literally means "Christmas Goat"—although the custom is the same—to dress in disguise and pay a visit to friends or neighbors, and let them guess the identity of the caller. The custom is reviving in Norway although practiced more by the children.

continuing with her explanation. Betsy, Bernt and Julius each took a turn at naming local friends and at every wrong guess, the visitors laughed and jumped, to make their bells ring even louder. Then Grandmother announced:

"I know who you are. Gust and Inga Olafson. And Oscar Huseth!"

"They are neighbors down the road," Ida said. "Oscar is the hired man."

Off came the ski caps and out came the coffee pot. Grandmother produced a plate of spritz cookies and krumkaka, a cone-shaped confection she had made that afternoon. While everyone was enjoying all this food and good fellowship, Florence felt a little cheated. Her mother never had celebrated Jule Bokk. She had thought all this foolishness was much too old-fashioned. When Isabelle had shocked the family by marrying a Swede, she had tossed out almost all the old Scandinavian traditions.

Florence heard another rap at the door. "Could this be more Jule Bokk?"

Betsy went to the door but instead of another Christmas Fool, there stood a wizened old lady dressed in a heavy woolen shawl, long skirt and boots. The visor of the man's cap she wore was pulled halfway over her face and a corncob pipe was clenched between her yellowed teeth.

"Oh, Lord," Ida sighed. "It's Ragnhild Lundquist. A friend of Mother's. That isn't a costume but her real clothes. Ragnhild couldn't think of trying to disguise herself. Not with that awful pipe she smokes all the time."

Betsy greeted her visitor and lit up her own pipe, exhaling the terrible smell of strong, rough-cut tobacco. Florence looked away, knowing that this was a source of embarrassment to Ida. Betsy didn't seem to care what Ida thought about it and enjoyed every puff.

"How about fixing us a hot toddy, Bernt?." Betsy asked. "I bet Florence never has tasted one before."

Bernt filled a teakettle with water and put it on the stove. Then he found a bottle of brandy in the cupboard and set out some coffee mugs. It was true that Florence never had tasted anything stronger than her mother's dandelion wine, other than her one experience with the chokecherry wine at the Togstaad Social. She felt in a holiday mood and very daring, and offered to try one.

She watched Bernt pour hot water into the mugs to warm them, then dump out the water and put an ounce of brandy into each mug, a little sugar and nutmeg, then add some hot water. He stirred the concoction, gave a mug to Florence and waited for her reaction. She took a tentative sip. The toddy felt warm and smooth going down and even warmer on her stomach.

"Why, Bernt. This is the best drink ever."

Her uncle beamed with pleasure and after serving the others, he set about cracking hazel nuts to share with the kitchen full of company.

"This is Bernt's favorite occupation," Ida said with a smile. "When he isn't out gathering nuts, he's shelling them. That's his idea of an interesting evening."

The next morning, after a hearty breakfast, there was popcorn to make. Ida poured a small handful of kernels into the wire popper and then shook it over the cookstove until every kernel was popped, only to repeat this chore again and again until an entire big bowl was filled. Meanwhile, using a sharp needle and some sturdy thread, Florence made the strings to hang on the Christmas tree, alternating between a kernel of popcorn and a bright red cranberry. Bernt and Julius had selected the finest spruce they could find out in the woods the day before, and now they set it up in the parlor.

"Did you have any time to go shopping?" Florence asked Ida as they decorated the tree.

"Oh heavens, no," Ida replied. "Our family doesn't go in much for presents, anyway. It's enough of a present just to come home for a little while. No one expects anything because no one has any money."

Florence felt a little relieved to hear that. She had bought a box of handkerchiefs for Grandmother and that had been the extent of her Christmas shopping.

That evening, Betsy made römmegrot—(RHEM-meh-gret). Using her big iron kettle, she poured in the richest cream she had been saving for this special kind of pudding. She added flour and with her long-handled wooden ladle, she drew out the butterfat that came to the top. This was served in bowls with nutmeg and cinnamon sprinkled over the top, for those who wanted more flavor. She served limpa bread, a home-baked rye and wheat mixture seasoned with molasses.

"This is so delicious, Grandmother," Florence said. "I wish I could send Minnie Knudson over here, for some cooking lessons. All she knows how to make is boiled meat and potatoes."

"Do you girls know there is a dance tonight over to the Olafson's?" Betsy asked. "Don't you want to go?"

"There is! Why didn't you tell us, Bernt?" Ida looked at her older brother with impatience. Sometimes his quiet ways were hard to bear.

"I know the Olafsons will expect me to play the fiddle and I feel a little tired. But if you two women are determined to go, and don't take too long to get ready, we can go."

Staging dances at a moment's notice was not too unusual in the country, where diversions were hard to find. All one needed to do was roll up the rug in the parlor and find someone to provide the music. Both Bernt and Julius were popular guests, as both could play the fiddle. Almost everyone in Betsy's musical family could play some instrument, Ida the piano and organ and Isabelle the mandolin.

Florence and Ida dashed upstairs to change while Bernt and Julius hitched up the horses. Florence loved to dance and had learned all the latest steps at the Normal. But out in the country, it was hard to find a partner who could do much more than a simple waltz or two-step.

The days slipped past and soon it was Christmas Eve. That meant time to cook lutefisk (LOO-ta-fisk). In Norway, the fish was cod but the Minnesota descendants settled for the whitefish they could catch in Monson Lake. Any fish would do, so long as it had been preserved in lye. The pungent odor as it bubbled in the kettle, was a vital part of the holiday atmosphere. Before the Reformation, the practice of eating fish on Christmas Eve was considered to be fasting. Martin Luther changed all that but the Norwegians still clung to the custom of lutefisk on Christmas Eve. It had to be boiled for just the right amount of time or it would fall apart, and that provoked much discussion in the kitchen. Lutefisk always was served with drawn butter, boiled russet potatoes and lefse. Betsy liked to add lingonberries to the menu, to cut the heaviness of the meal.

After they had dined on all these delicacies, it was time to open the gifts. Bernt and Julius offered little packages of hazelnuts to the womenfolk. Ida, who was clever with a needle, had made a muslin apron for Betsy, with red cross-stitching on the bib area, and the little side pocket and the hem. Florence, who never had learned how to embroider, gave her grandmother a box of three dainty handkerchiefs purchased at a store. Betsy had knit winter scarves and mittens for everyone. Good food was more important to this family, than gifts.

Later that evening, they set off for Sunburg and the Lutheran church for midnight service. Florence had seen this little clapboard church before, with its rustic, hand-carved pews, hand-made altar cloths and vestments, and furnished with well-thumbed hymn books printed in the old-time Norwegian script. The grim-faced pastor conducted the service in "high Norwegian" and of course, Florence couldn't understand a word. She recognized some of the hymns and could hum along, feeling surrounded by memories of ancestors who had worshipped in this very church so long ago. Great-grandfather Hans, one of the

Florence

founders, now rested in the church graveyard along with his wife, Ingeborg, under a tombstone covered with lichen.

Florence gave thanks to God for her many blessings— for these hardy ancestors who had been guided by the dream of a new and better life for their children and their children's children; for Ida, her best friend and mentor; and for Grandmother Betsy, a living link between the old ways and the new. She prayed for the strength to get through the remaining months under the Knudson roof and for the welfare of her brothers and sisters, the younger ones still at home with Isabelle in Fargo and the older ones who had ventured west, deeper into the wilds of North Dakota. The most recent letter from Clara, her oldest sister, had given her cause to worry. Clara had married a homesteader and now was living like a pioneer of olden days, out on the prairie. Florence shuddered. She would never, ever marry a rancher or a farmer. If she ever married at all, which for the present time looked rather doubtful, she would marry someone who lived in a city.

The happy Christmas vacation came to an end all too soon, and it was time to bid farewell to Grandmother. There was new snow on the ground, just the right amount for Bernt to take Ida and Florence back to their boarding places by horse-drawn sled.

As her uncle had predicted, the long, cold Minnesota winter had arrived.

Chapter Five

The Year 1913

Through deep snow, with her skirt hiked above her knees, Florence trudged across the pasture early Monday morning. Around the tops of her boots that came only to mid-calf, she could feel cold wet circles seeping into her long woolen underwear. It wasn't hard to imagine the giggles from the children when they would see her very private garment hung up to dry near the coal stove. Snow, she decided, was not so much fun now that she was a grown up.

As the schoolhouse came into view, Florence stopped short in her tracks with a gasp of dismay. She saw the two windows, the ones that had been covered with butcher paper, were now sealed shut with heavy thick boards. Before leaving on vacation, she had written a letter of protest to Mr. Hagen, the treasurer, and had begged him to reconsider the board's decision about the windows. Evidently, her thoughts on the subject had made no impression. The windows had been boarded up anyway.

Feeling discouraged, Florence climbed the steps to the schoolhouse, unlocked the door and shook the snow from her boots. The cloakroom was so cold she could see her breath and she hurried to light a fire in the coal stove.

While waiting for the room to warm up, she took a closer look at the sheets of thick butcher paper tacked up inside the windows. She simply had to find a way to repair this disaster. But how?

Other teachers had box socials to raise money but those auctions could bring in only six or seven dollars. That was not near enough for window glass, but a box social would tie in nicely with a Valentine program. Once she had all the parents gathered together, she could make an impassioned plea for donations. That might do the trick. But that would mean going over the heads of the school board. Could she dare risk it? She was having enough trouble with the school board as it was.

Florence weighed all the possibilities, as she stripped off her woolen tights and hung them over a chair next to the stove. Then she studied the list of promises that had been written on the blackboard. She would need to go over them one by one with the children, before beginning a discussion of the Valentine program. The idea of a spelling bee popped into her head. Florence loved spelling bees and a competition might be just the thing to lure Ralph Huston out of his shell.

Before she knew it, the hands on the clock pointed to nine. Florence rolled up her slightly damp woolens and put them in a desk drawer, out of sight of the children, and went outside to ring the school bell. "Time for class to begin," she called. "We have a lot to talk about today so let's hurry and take our seats."

As the children filed into the cloakroom, Florence noted with satisfaction the absence of Tom Clayton. That was one thing to be grateful for, she thought, as she stepped up on the platform to ring the bell. The opening exercises began and when they were almost finished, cloakroom door banged open. Tom Clayton lumbered in and clomped his way to his desk. The children giggled and turned around to stare. Florence ignored him and called on Alta to stand up and read aloud the list of promises on the blackboard. Looking pleased to be assigned this task, Alta read the promises in her high piping voice and not a sound came from the back of the room.

Florence erased the board. "I want to be sure everyone is in agreement before we talk about the Valentine program. Let's see a show of hands."

Feeling satisfied now, she wrote in big cursive letters: The District 34 Valentine Program. She turned around to ask, "Who has an idea for the program?"

Selma Knudson raised her hand. "Let's make red paper hearts."

Harriet Hagen raised her hand. "Let's write some pretty verses for the Valentines and give them to our parents."

The others had suggestions about the kind of cookies to bring and how big a Valentine box they should have. Everyone but Tom bubbled with enthusiasm. "Can we do all this before Valentine's Day?" Alta asked anxiously.

"It will be a big project, but we can set aside some class time every day to work on the program. For example, we can estimate the amount of construction paper I will need to buy. That can count as arithmetic class. The verses we write can count for composition and penmanship. Now what do you think about having a spelling bee too?" She looked straight at Ralph. "How many have taken part in a spelling bee before?"

Not one child raised a hand. "What about you, Ralph? You're such a good speller."

The Fifth Grader's face turned crimson. "No, never, Miss Thompson."

"That's too bad. Spelling bees are such fun. We can form two teams and have spell down. I'll talk to the school board about getting a prize for the best speller of all. Now how many want to be on a team?"

At the mention of a prize, several hands shot up. Ralph hunched down in his desk as if he were trying to become invisible. Florence wrote the names of the children who wanted to participate on the blackboard, and then looked at her potential scholar. "I'd like to see you for a few minutes after class, Ralph. We need to have a private talk."

The morning routine continued with no opportunity to rescue her long underwear from the desk drawer. That meant a chilly walk to the Knudson's for lunch before she could exchange the damp woolens for some dry ones. Afternoon classes proceeded and Ralph kept his face hidden behind a book. He hovered near the cloakroom door after everyone had gone, and asked, "You wanted to see me, Miss Thompson?"

"Come sit next to my desk, Ralph. Tell me, why didn't you raise your hand to be on the spelling team? All your written work is outstanding. Don't you know you are the best speller in the school?"

"I—I couldn't be on the team, Miss Thompson. Please don't ask me."

He was a good-looking child, slim and well built, with an unruly thatch of sandy hair and blue intelligent eyes. He didn't seem to have the slightest idea of what a bright student he was.

"Please think about being on the team. We need you to take part in this."

"I—I just can't, Miss Thompson." Ralph looked as if he might faint.

"Please think about it, Ralph." She smiled and didn't press him any further.

Three weeks flew by. The hulking presence of Tom Clayton haunted her days and the dread of a confrontation with Mr. Togstaad stalked her dreams at night. Heavy dark clouds filled the winter skies and made the classroom so dim, the children had to take turns to study around the light of her kerosene lamp. Finally, she'd had enough of that and on a Thursday evening in late January, she called the local operator for the Togstaad party line number.

"Hello? Mr. Togstaad? This is Miss Thompson calling. I need to talk with you about a very important matter. Could I come to your house on Saturday morning?"

"It's a long vay over here," he hedged. "And I'm very busy."

"I can borrow Mr. Knudson's wagon. I won't take more than a few minutes of your time."

Reluctantly, he agreed and just as reluctantly, Carl hitched up the wagon on Saturday morning. "Helmer Togstaad is not going to change his mind about anything," Carl announced, after she had told him about the importance of her mission. "Not about the windows. Not about anything. You vill be wasting your time."

"I don't think so," Florence replied, and urged the horses on their way. Most of the snow on the roads had melted and as she made her way though the dirty slush, she mentally prepared herself. There had to be some way to break through his icy composure and she prayed for the right words to come. After tying up the reins to the porch rail, she swallowed hard and knocked on his door.

"Come in, Miss Thompson," the chairman said, an amused smile on his face. "This was a long drive, yust to see me." He was dressed in the same Sunday suit he had worn at the Social, and his manner was just as condescending as he ushered her into his chilly parlor. It wasn't hard to tell there was no mother in this house. Everything looked out of place, books and papers scattered on the tables and floor, pictures askew on the walls.

"So what is on your mind that is so important, Miss Thompson?" He sat in his rocking chair while Florence found a place on the stiff Victorian settee.

"I'm sure you know that District 34 is a difficult school," she said, coming right to the point. "Carl Knudson is no help at all. He never discusses anything with me."

"Carl has been boarding the teacher for too many years. That's the only thing I can agree about with him."

"The children are doing well," Florence continued. "Your son Erik could do better in reading class if you would spend some time with him. Read to him. Show him that you care. He's a very lonely child."

"I don't have time for such things. I have a farm to run. I depend upon you to teach him how to read."

"You could help, Mr. Togstaad. Parents are just as important as teachers. But I came to see you about some other things. One is the Valentine program I plan to have. The other is about new window glass. You have no idea how dark the classroom is now. The children can hardly see to study their lessons."

Togstaad cleared this throat. "The school board has no money for such things as window glass. Someday soon, ve will build a new schoolhouse closer to my place. For now, boarding up the vindows is the best ve could do."

"But it could be years before you build a new school. If a new one is built at all. What about today? Don't you want your own son to learn how to read?"

"You are an upstart of a girl, Miss Thompson. Going on and on about vindow glass. You don't understand the situation at District 34."

Florence felt a new stir of anger. She hated being treated as a child. She had the responsibilities of an adult and then some. This cold fish of a man didn't know a thing about education and yet, as chairman, he held all the power in the school district. It wasn't right. Wasn't fair.

"I understand more than you think, Mr. Togstaad. Miss Thorson told me all about your feud with Carl Knudson. Both of you are very wrong. If you won't spend any money on the schoolhouse, then I will raise some myself. I'm going to have a Valentine program with a box social. And you could help sell tickets," she added impulsively. The ticket idea had just sprung into her head and almost at once, she realized she had made a terrible mistake. She had pushed him too far.

"Sell tickets!" The color drained from his face. "I never heard of such a thing."

"You are always opposed to new ideas. I can see that. So be stubborn, Mr. Togstaad. Don't help me. Let the poor students sit in the dark. Let the schoolbooks fall to pieces and don't ever buy new ones. Don't fill up that horrible mud hole in the schoolyard. Have everything your way.

And good luck in finding a teacher for next year because you can be sure, I won't be back."

Florence marched out the front door and into the cold January air. She untied the horses, climbed up to the seat of the wagon and tried valiantly to calm herself. She had ruined her big chance to get some help from Helmer Togstaad. She had thrown into his face everything that was wrong about the school and she should have realized that no self-respecting Norwegian farmer would dream of selling tickets to a school affair. Whatever had she been thinking? A teacher is not supposed to talk this way to the chairman of the school board.

"Miss Thompson! Vait!" Helmer Togstaad had put on his winter jacket and now he was striding toward her. He grabbed the bridle of one horse and gave it a yank. "You don't understand everything about District 34. It is impossible to have a program there. The young men around here are roughnecks. They will break it up. I've seen it happen before. There's no controlling these young hooligans."

Florence sat back on the wagon bench and felt as if the fire had gone out of her. Miss Thorson, in her long recital of woes, had left out a few things about District 34. Ruffians in the neighborhood? She hadn't heard that one before. From her perch on the wagon seat, Florence looked down at Helmer Togstaad.

"If what you say is true, then I will need your help even more. I have promised the children we would have a Valentine program. I can't let them down just because of a few troublemakers. Can't something be done to stop them? Why couldn't you and the other school board members stand guard. We need to let these rough boys know they can't run District 34."

Togstaad's grip on the bridle tightened. A muscle twitched in his cheek. Florence knew these Norwegian farmers didn't change their minds very often about anything. But now, praise God, the chairman seemed to be softening a little.

"Mr. Togstaad," she continued, "a promise made, should be a promise kept. The children are so excited about having this program."

His hand on the bridle relaxed a little. "Vell, Miss Thompson, I must say I admire your spunk and vinegar. If you want to have a program that much, then I vill help you. I vill ask the school board to stand guard. But I'm not going to promise anything about vindow glass. And I am not going to sell tickets."

"But you and the school board will stand guard and keep the peace."

"Ja. I can do that much."

Florence felt overcome with relief. "Thank you, Mr. Togstaad. I will telephone you about the details and take care of everything else."

"Ve vill bring baseball bats. Vill that suit you?" A wisp of a smile played around his thin lips and there was a new, almost respectful expression in his eyes.

"Baseball bats! What a wonderful idea. That would suit me very well, Mr. Togstaad." Florence drove off, feeling a little burst of triumph. Getting this much help from the school board was a major victory.

During these preparations for the Valentine program, Florence spent every weekend possible with Ida. She wasn't going to stay marooned at the Knudson farm, not so long as there was Augaton and his Ford. He was still sweet on Ida, unaware of the competition looming on the horizon, but would he agree to take them to a dance? She had read in the *Benson Review* about the dances held almost every Saturday night at the Town Hall, but Augaton was a little shy and not much for dancing. This would take some major planning to talk him into it. Then, suddenly, an idea popped into her head. Bachelors liked to be invited for dinner and that would be a good way to pay him back for all the favors he had done. She couldn't afford a dinner at a restaurant but what about having a dinner party right here at the Knudson's? Afterward, the three of them could go to the dance and let Carl think the trio was going to the Quale's house, as they did so often. As Ida used to say, no one would be the wiser.

"Of course I will pay Minnie for preparing the dinner," Florence said when she discussed the plan with Ida on the telephone. "I think Minnie will do it for a dollar."

"You are a regular spendthrift," Ida replied. "I know Augaton likes a home-cooked meal and if I ask him very sweetly, I'm sure he will take us to the dance."

Everything fell into place. Minnie agreed to serve roast chicken with all the trimmings and Florence started counting the days until Saturday. She loved to dance and since she was so new in the county, hardly anyone there would know she was a schoolteacher. It was unlikely that any word about it would get back to Carl. When Ida and Augaton arrived in the Ford that Saturday, amid a chorus of squawks from the chickens, Florence dashed outside to greet them with still another bright idea.

"Ida, I'll make a wager with you," Florence said as her aunt got out of the car. "This is such a special occasion,

I'll bet a quarter I can get Minnie or Carl to loosen up and say something at supper tonight."

Ida laughed. "Don't count on it. This will be easy money for me."

"Thanks for inviting us to dinner," Augaton said, shooing off the dog that kept circling the car. "I'm looking forward to it."

"Just remember," Florence said. "Don't say one word to Carl about where we're going later. It's really none of his business."

Minnie had set the table in the dining room. As usual, Mrs. Knudson sat at one end in her wheelchair, engrossed in her knitting. Carl sat at the opposite end, looking like a country squire in a clean shirt with a napkin tucked under his chin. Florence found a place next to Ida on one side, with Augaton opposite her. On the table was a platter of roast chicken cut into serving-size pieces, a big bowl of mashed potatoes, plus another bowl of corn cut from the cob with a dish of melted butter nearby. It was obvious that Minnie had outdone herself. This was the kind of meal usually reserved for Sundays.

Minnie gave a sullen look to the guests and went back to the kitchen for a dish of cucumber pickles and a plate loaded with slices of freshly baked bread. Then she sat down next to Augaton. Taking this as a signal to begin, Florence picked up her linen napkin and turned to Carl. "Do you plan to go to the school board meeting on Sunday week? Mr. Togstaad is going to ask all the members to stand guard at my Valentine program. In case of trouble."

She looked squarely at Carl, at his big leathery face and bushy dark beard. His eyes widened a bit and then, solemn as an owl, he reached for the bowl of potatoes.

Ida cleared her throat and gave Florence a knowing little "I told you so" kind of smile. Around the table, three pairs of Knudson eyes stared at the teachers—unblinking, inscrutable. Exactly like owls. Thoughts of her foolish optimistic wager circled in her head and suddenly, without any warning, a silly little giggle rose up from the pit of her stomach. Florence put her hand over her mouth to stop it; but there the giggle was—rising up anyway. The clock in the kitchen began to make its tardy announcement of the hour, with a sonorous bong . . . bong . . . like a chime sounding from an ancient tomb. With a helpless shrug, lips pressed together, Florence dug into her pocket for a quarter. Bong, bong, went the clock. Click, click, click, answered the knitting needles. Florence slid the coin next to Ida's plate, trying to hold back another insistent schoolgirl giggle.

Ida glanced down at the quarter and began to laugh, her shoulders shaking as she hunched them together, trying to control herself. A bewildered look passed across Augaton's face. The eyes stared. Florence burst into laughter that was not the least bit ladylike and there was nothing she could do to stop it. She tried her best to stop, but now it was too late. The laughter just kept coming. When she caught Ida's eye, that only made things worse.

Blank-faced, Minnie and Carl stared from one teacher to the other, as if the two had suddenly taken leave of their senses. Helpless with laughter, Florence threw her napkin down, pushed away from the table and dashed up the narrow stairway to her room. She fell on her bed, tears rolling down her face. A few seconds later, Ida burst into the room and threw herself on the bed too, seized by a paroxysm of uncontrollable laughter.

Florence

"Those eyes!" she gasped. "Staring at us. I warned you I would win the bet."

Florence pulled herself up on one elbow. "You won fair and square, anyway. We acted like idiots and not one of them said a word."

Ida sat up, her long dress in a tangle. "What are you going to do about Carl? He must think we've both gone crazy."

"I don't care what he thinks. Living here is enough to drive anyone crazy. It's a great wonder I haven't gone crazy before this."

Florence got up to pour some water from the pitcher into her basin. She washed her face, dusted a little rice powder on her nose and combed her hair. "Let's forget about dinner. I couldn't eat a thing after all this. Let's go."

Ida went to the mirror to straighten her hair and polish her spectacles. "That's all right with me. If Augaton has finished eating, let's go."

They trooped downstairs to find Carl Knudson stationed near the kitchen door, looking like thunder. "Miss Thompson, your friend here, Mr. Jorgenson, yust told me something I can hardly believe. That you folks are going to that sinful dance in Benson tonight. Is that true?"

Florence shot a look at Augaton. The betrayer. What could have possessed him to spill the beans like that?

"Yes, it's true. I'm going to the dance with my aunt and Mr. Jorgenson and I don't see anything sinful about it. Go tell the school board if you want to. Now, if you will step out of my way, we will go. Ida and I will be staying at the Quale place tonight. Thank you for the lovely dinner. Now goodnight."

She put on her coat and grabbed Ida by the arm. In a few more minutes, out in the yard, Augaton appeared to crank up the Ford. "I don't know what that was all about," he said. "You two missed a very good dinner."

Florence held her tongue. Augaton had been so generous, taking her places in his motorcar, she decided not to question him about what he had said to Carl. So much went right over Augaton's head, especially stupid rules about what teachers could and could not do in their limited social lives.

"Well Ida, I won the bet after all," Florence said when they were on their way to Benson. "Carl Knudson said a mouthful about going to the dance. So you'd better give back the quarter."

"Florence, you are the limit. You don't hesitate a minute about speaking your mind. You probably will need that quarter, at the rate you are going."

Florence didn't lack for dancing partners at the Town Hall and she had a wonderful time. All day Sunday, between hands of whist, she joked with the Quales about her first attempt to give a dinner party, and what a disaster it was.

"You could have had your dinner party here," Alice said. "Just you and Ida and Augaton. Why didn't you ask me?"

"I didn't want to make any trouble for you," Florence replied. "If I ever have a dinner party again, I'll do it when I have a home of my own." She looked around at the Quale's cozy house and hoped that someday, someday that dream might come true; that she could meet the right man and stop living out of a trunk. Would that day ever come? She was beginning to wonder.

The following Monday, during morning recess, Florence stood at the schoolhouse window watching the children at play. For the hundredth time, she wondered why Tom Clayton bothered to come to school at all. On this day, he looked even more sullen and out of place than usual and with a sense of foreboding, she watched him saunter over to the swings where the beginning readers had gathered. Suddenly, and for no apparent reason, he grabbed Erik Togstaad by the collar of his jacket and pushed him to the ground. Erik set up a howl of protest. Instinctively, Florence rapped on the window. Then she marched outdoors, over the sprinkle of snow on the ground, and ordered the troublemaker into the schoolhouse.

"I have warned you, Tom. And now I'm finished with you. For good. I can't have you hurting the little ones. You don't belong here anyway. You are expelled."

Tom hung his head. "I'm sorry, teacher."

"It's a little late for that, Tom. Why do you bother to come to school at all? You never study anything. You don't contribute anything. You're old enough to quit school."

Tom stared at the little puddles flowing from his wet boots. Florence knew that self-expression didn't come easy to the farm boys but she felt more than a little curious. "You know you don't belong here," she repeated.

"I—I guess I don't. If you really want to know, I just wanted to see what you were like, Miss Thompson."

"What I was like? That's all you wanted?"

"I'd heard you were just a kid. You're so much younger than all the other teachers we've had here. That's all."

"That's all? There must be more to it than that."

"Well, I guess I wanted to get off the farm for a while.

Have someplace to go. But don't worry about me anymore, Miss Thompson. I won't be back."

Tom straightened his shoulders and executed a snappy salute, the way he had done on his first day at school. Then he marched out the door like a stiff-legged soldier and didn't look back. She walked to the window to see him cross the schoolyard and give one last kick to the rusty seesaw. He turned for a moment and seeing Florence still at the window, he raised his big shoulders in a hopeless shrug. Then the tall figure disappeared into a clump of trees.

A sense of emptiness and failure swept over Florence. Tom would never change and there was nothing she could do about it. If there ever had been any opportunity to help him, that would have existed years before, back when he had just started school. But no one had bothered and now it was too late. In her imagination, she could visualize Ralph Huston a few years from now, frustrated and adrift because no one cared, becoming another misfit like Tom Clayton, disappointed by life, his zest for learning extinguished. Ralph was far brighter than Tom, with much more to offer, and so his loss would be even more devastating. Something needed to be done about his problem right now. There had to be a way to reach him, to help him overcome his self-consciousness. Florence felt determined to give it another try.

Plans hummed along about the Valentine program and Florence continued to ask Ralph to stand up and recite during geography and in spelling class. Ralph continued to stammer and hide his face in his book. Once again, she asked him to stay for a few minutes after class.

"Ralph, I want to congratulate you on the fine work you are doing," Florence said when they were alone. "I know you don't like to recite but other than that, you are my very best student."

Ralph blushed, his eyes moist with pleasure.

"It's true. You are. I'd like you to be captain of the spelling team."

"You want me? To be captain? Oh, I couldn't, Miss Thompson."

"You can do it. We can practice after school. Just the two of us. Then reciting in front of the class will get much easier. I promise."

"I—I'd be too scared. I might make a mistake. You'd better get someone else. How about my sister? Alta would make a good captain."

"I want you, Ralph. Alta has agreed to be captain of the opposing team. How about inviting her to join us with these special sessions. Would that make you feel better?"

"A little. I guess."

Florence paused, searching for the right words to say. "Do you know I used to feel shy in school, too. Just like you. Then a favorite teacher told me that no one expected me to be perfect all the time. It was all right to make mistakes. Everybody makes them. The trick is not to feel afraid to make a mistake."

The color drained from Ralph's face and he took a few quick breaths.

"Let's practice with one word. Just one. Spell 'practice' for me."

"P-R-A-C-T-I-C-E." Ralph said the letters slowly, his gaze fixed on a spot in the ceiling.

"That's very good. Now let's look at the spelling book and see if you can spell all the words we learned in class today."

Ralph spelled all the words on the list without hesitation. Then he spelled all the words from the previous day, and the previous week. He hadn't forgotten one of them.

"You have such a good memory! Now, when you get home tonight, will you study the words for tomorrow? Extra hard. Then when I call on you, will you stand up and spell just one word on the list? Will you promise me that? And then decide for yourself about becoming the captain. We will have extra time after class starting tomorrow. You and Alta. Every day. Is that a bargain?"

The corners of Ralph's mouth turned upward in a shy smile. Florence guessed that no one ever had offered to spend extra time with him on his schoolwork. His parents had such a big family, with younger children at home. There wasn't enough time to go around.

"All right, Miss Thompson. That's a bargain. I'll let you know later about being captain."

"In time for the Valentine program?"

"Maybe. I have to go now. It's almost time for chores. I'll see you tomorrow."

Florence watched him go, knowing she had just taken a first step in a long journey. Could she draw him out of his shell? Only time would tell about that.

Excitement mounted as January melted into February. The children rehearsed songs, made Valentines with construction paper and composed verses. Florence wrote invitations to the parents for the children to take home, along with advice on what to bring for the box social. Taking a cue from the way Ida did things, she put a notice in the *Benson Review* about the program. Florence and Ralph and Alta worked on extra credit assignments, laughed together and looked up words in the dictionary just for fun. Watching Ralph grow in self-confidence was its own reward and when she felt he was ready, she asked him once again about being captain of the spelling team.

"Are you sure you want me?" he asked. "I've never been captain of anything before."

"Well, this is your chance. You will be a wonderful captain and I'm sure you will make everyone at District 34 feel very proud."

He smiled without a trace of a blush this time. "I hope so, Miss Thompson. I never thought that I would like to stay after school. Now I kind of hate to think about when this will all be over."

The night before the big program finally arrived. The weather had been unusually mild for the past few days, and Florence prayed it would stay that way.

She prayed the Valentine program would be a success. After all this work to prepare, it just had to be.

Leonard Kvam
Willmar Academy graduation picture

Chapter Six

The Valentine Program

On Friday, snow began to fall in the morning and by mid-afternoon, prospects were going from bad to worse for the Valentine program. The classroom was in readiness with big red hearts pasted on the walls and a decorated cardboard box sitting on the teacher's desk. Five adult-size chairs had been placed in front of the room for the school board members. A buzz of happy anticipation filled the air but the snowfall didn't give any sign of stopping very soon.

"I'm going to dismiss class a little early today," Florence said. "Be sure to put your best thinking caps on this evening for the spelling bee. I'll see you promptly at seven o'clock."

Ingeborg raised her hand. "What if we get snowed in, Miss Thompson? And we can't get to school?"

"Then we'll have to postpone the program, won't we? We can have it later on, when the weather clears." Florence smiled reassuringly, although she knew a postponement would be a big letdown. The children were primed for tonight.

After everyone had gone, she banked the fire in the coal stove, locked the door and walked outside to inspect the snow-covered road. People in Minnesota had gotten through worse than this, she thought. It would take a blizzard to keep them at home. Picking up her skirts, she started across the pasture, leaving deep tracks with her boots.

In Minnie's kitchen, she made two sandwiches from leftover pork roast, using a little homemade mustard from the pantry. Minnie watched with her arms folded while the knitting needles clicked from the direction of the wheelchair in the corner. Mrs. Knudson had produced enough woolen scarves to keep the entire state of Minnesota warm, and now she was starting on squares for an afghan.

"I see you have baked a sponge cake," Florence said to Minnie. "Would it be all right if I take a couple of slices for the social?" Florence had lined a shoebox with waxed paper and now she put in the wrapped sandwiches. Minnie nodded her assent so she added the cake and two linen napkins. She wrapped the box in some pink tissue paper she had been saving and tied it with a long red satin ribbon. "I hope someone exciting will buy this."

According to custom, the person who offered the highest bid would get to dine with one who had brought the box supper. This was an excellent way for folks to meet one another, and a favorite way for local bachelors to court available young ladies. But sometimes, the system didn't work. Sometimes a young lady ended up with a bachelor she didn't care for at all.

After finishing her own box, Florence made some sandwiches for Carl to take for his supper. He probably wouldn't bid on anyone's box, but he couldn't get out of attending the program. He'd never hear the end of it, if he didn't show up and do his part to keep the peace. Florence dabbed a little mustard on Carl's sandwich, humming to herself to keep up her spirits. This evening simply *had* to be a success.

Upstairs in her chilly bedroom, Florence changed into a fresh shirtwaist and pinned her curly hair into a bun in back. She had a strong hunch that Leonard Kvam might turn up that evening. He was the kind of person who read the newspapers, and he just might be home from school that weekend.

The landscape was shrouded in white when Florence picked her way across the pasture. She needed to arrive early to be sure the coal stove had not sputtered out, leaving the classroom icy cold. As she drew closer, she saw the glow of lamplight in the schoolhouse windows and a curl of smoke rising from the chimney.

Someone was already there! It had to be someone with a key but whoever would take all the trouble to arrive early? Florence hurried her step. When she entered the classroom, much to her astonishment, she found Helmer Togstaad with Erik at his side, warming his hands at the coal stove.

"Good evening, Miss Thompson. I thought I would come early to see about the stove." Togstaad wore his best suit with the fancy vest and pocket watch. Erik looked as if he had just been scrubbed within an inch of his life.

"I can't tell you how wonderful it is, to see you so interested in my program," Florence said. She and Togstaad had talked on the telephone a few times about some details concerning the program, but Florence hadn't seen the chairman since the day of their confrontation.

The Valentine Program

Now he seemed to be an entirely different person, smiling and friendly.

"You deserve some help, young lady. You have done vonders with these children in yust the few weeks you have been here. My Erik knows the entire alphabet now. He can read the little storybooks you sent home with him. I'm very grateful."

Florence could hardly believe her ears. It was true that Erik's reading had improved. He could do almost as well as Ingeborg, who had parents who doted on her and couldn't do enough to help. She guessed that Mr. Togstaad must be reading to Erik at home, although he would be too proud to admit it.

Just then, footsteps sounded in the cloakroom amid greetings in Norwegian. The school board members had arrived along with their families. Now as they entered the classroom, Florence could see the men waving their base-ball bats over their heads and joking with one another. Mr. Hagen, the treasurer, had brought his buggy whip and he cracked it on the wood floor with a resounding whack. The wives jumped and the children giggled and asked him to do it again.

Even Mr. Togstaad was laughing as he ushered the men to the chairs in front, while the wives gathered around the coal stove to make coffee. More arrivals came by the wagonload, to put their decorated lunch boxes on her desk and give her a hearty handshake. Florence found a minute to whisper into Mr. Togstaad's ear. "It looks like we will be ready for whatever might happen tonight."

"You can bet ve vill," he answered with a grim smile.

By now, the classroom was filled to overflowing. Pupils sat two or three to a desk and parents lined the classroom walls. Other young people in the area were present, drawn by the fun of bidding on the decorated boxes. Feeling thrilled by the big turnout in spite of the heavy snowfall, Florence stepped up to the platform and rang her bell.

"Welcome, everyone. Parents, pupils and friends. We will start in the same way we begin every school day. We will sing, *My Country 'Tis of Thee.*"

The children filed up to the front and launched into the first verse they knew so well. Then, in the midst of the second verse, the cloakroom door flew open with a loud crash. Nine big teenage boys barged into the tiny room. They wore heavy hunting boots and woolen jackets and caps pulled down to partially conceal their faces. In a flurry of stomping boots, they lined themselves up against the bookshelves. It was hard to tell for certain in the dim lamplight, but Florence was sure she could recognize one of the intruders slouching against the wall. It was Tom Clayton, with that same oafish grin on his face

Some of the mothers gasped in alarm and turned to stare at the boys. Florence felt a shiver of fear. She could taste the tension in the air, the kind of tension that could erupt in a free-for-all at any moment. She had to seize control and not let that happen. With heart beating in quick staccato, she ignored the unwelcome visitors and rang the long-handled school bell.

"We have learned a new song the children would like to sing for you," Florence announced. "It's easy and fun. The name of the tune is *Down by the Old Mill Stream.*" She blew the soft opening note on her pitch pipe. They had not even begun to sing when an ear-shattering catcall sounded from the back of the room and the steady rhythm of stomping feet grew louder . . . stomp, stomp, stomp. Then one of the boys let out a piercing whistle. Another followed. And another.

"All right you boys," Florence shouted above the racket. "You've had your chance to show off for everyone. Either you behave yourselves right this minute or clear out. I mean what I say. I have the school board here to back me up."

The five burly school board farmers rose to their feet and faced the back of the room. Each one waved his baseball bat in the air—Mr. Togstaad, Mr. Hagen, Mr. Christenson, Mr.Rodahl and Carl Knudson. Mr. Hagen lifted the handle of his buggy whip over his head, as if ready thrash the first offending scoundrel. Within seconds, the commotion ceased.

"You boys in the back . . . Now can you see what I mean?" Florence said. "We are going to continue this program in peace."

She raised the pitch pipe to her lips, blew the note again and commenced to sing in a clear strong voice. The children chimed in, hesitantly at first and then with more assurance. Some of the adults picked up the tune and others added the harmony. Slowly, silently, the intruders began to slip out the cloakroom door, one by one. Tom Clayton was the last to leave, but not until he had turned to the teacher and executed one last snappy salute.

Florence breathed a sigh of relief. She had avoided a tense situation without anyone getting hurt. She looked at the cloakroom door again to be sure all the troublemakers were gone and then, in the shadows, she saw a tall man enter in a furtive manner. A very tall young man with a hat in his hand. And a smile on his face. It was Leonard Kvam! Her heart jumped a beat. He had made a special effort to come to her program! The audience kept on singing and then the room exploded in applause. *Down by the Old Mill Stream* was a big hit.

"Thank you so much," Florence said with a warm smile in the direction of Leonard. "Next on the program is the reading of the Valentines written by the children." She reached into the decorated box and pulled out the first envelope. "This one is for Mr. Togstaad. Will Erik come up to read it for everyone?"

Full of confidence, Erik read his verse aloud and then delivered the red lacy Valentine to his father. The rest of the children each had a turn to be the center of attention. This part of the program was a huge success with round after round of applause.

The spelling bee followed. Ralph lined up his team of four and Alta lined up hers on the platform. Florence read the words to spell and kept score on the blackboard. Ralph's performance held everyone spellbound. He didn't miss a single word. When it came time for the audience to vote for the best speller with a show of hands, there was no question about who had won the Championship Award. Ralph went up to collect the prize, a crisp new one-dollar bill donated by the General Store in Benson.

"Now it's time to auction the lunch boxes," Florence announced. "Remember, all the money we raise will go for improvements to the schoolhouse. It's about time we get some new window glass, for one thing. So please be as generous as you can. Who will bid a dime for this beautiful box created by Alta Huston?"

She held up a shoe box decorated with hearts and long ribbons. That one sold quickly to Alta's father for fifty cents. Another box sold and another, for equally high prices. At the end of the auction, Florence picked up her own decorated box. Trying not to look directly at Leonard, she asked: "Do I hear a dime?"

"Seventy-five cents!" The shout came from Helmer Togstaad seated in the front row, an outrageous amount for two pork sandwiches and two pieces of sponge cake. No one could hope to top such a bid.

"Sold!" she said. "Now it's time to eat." Everyone settled down and while Helmer Togstaad stood in line for coffee, Florence spread out the lunch on her desk and started to count the coins she had collected.

"This was a fine program," Togstaad said when he came to join her.

"Should I give this money to Mr. Hagen now?" she asked. "I'm afraid it isn't enough for window glass. But the program went very well, thanks to you."

"You keep that money for yourself, Miss Thompson." Mr. Togstaad took Erik on his lap. "How much did you pay out of your own pocket for this program, for the construction paper and the crayons and such things. I know the school board hasn't been any too quick about providing extra money for you."

Once again, Florence could hardly believe her ears. The school board never had given her a dime, no matter how many requests she had submitted for funds. It was true that she had paid for everything out of her own pocket.

"I don't feel right about taking this. I told everyone the money would go for improvements to the schoolhouse."

"And so it has. Many fine improvements. You keep the money. And I keep my beautiful Valentine from my Erik. I don't want to hear anything more about it. Ve can think about vindowglass another time."

Florence blinked back a tear. She never had thought in her wildest dreams, that a man like Helmer Togstaad, so rooted in the old stubborn Norwegian ways, could ever become her friend. And now here he was, expressing gratitude in his own way, insisting she should keep this little hoard of coins. She couldn't speak. And then, just at that moment, she looked up to see Leonard standing next to her, a whimsical smile on his face.

"May I see you home, Miss Thompson? I brought the cutter and it's just right for the new snow. How about it?"

"That sounds very nice, Mr. Kvam," she answered, feeling a little flustered. She introduced him to the school board chairman. "But first, I need to help put the furniture back in place and tidy up the classroom."

"You go with your young man, Miss Thompson," Helmer Togstaad said. "I vill take care of everything here and lock up. The school board can help me."

With that matter decided, Florence thanked all the guests and children for a successful evening. She put on her hat and coat, not stopping to think what people might say. It was her business if she wanted to go for a short sleigh ride without a chaperone. She couldn't see anything wrong with that.

A few minutes later, she joined Leonard at the schoolhouse door. They stepped outside, into the crisp night air. The snowfall had stopped and now a bright moon hung in the night sky, surrounded by a blanket of stars. Taking her hand, Leonard led her past the collection of horses and wagons in the schoolyard, and over to his sleek, black open cutter. It was set up high on gleaming metal runners and hitched to a beautiful horse that whinnied and tossed his head, while his nostrils sent up little smoke signals into the cold night air.

"That was quite a show you put on this evening," Leonard said, tucking the blanket around her. "I liked the way you stood up to those ruffians. You certainly put them in their place in a hurry." He sounded half-teasing, half-admiring.

"Don't give me too much credit," she said. "I had everything worked out ahead of time with the school board members. Mr. Togstaad knew I might have trouble and I certainly did."

"Your program was wonderful. I don't remember ever seeing such a great spell down, when I was in grammar school. I'm just sorry I couldn't buy your box supper tonight. As usual, I'm a little short of money."

"I've never been in a cutter before. I hear they go very fast. This won't be like riding in my uncle's wooden sled, I'm sure. Just don't dump me in a snow bank."

Leonard slipped in next to her. "Don't worry about that. Now hang on." He flicked the whip over the horse's head and they were off in a swirl of snow.

"You promised not to drive so fast," Florence said, clutching her hat.

He slowed the pace to a gentle walk. "Sorry. I was just showing off. This cutter can really go and I thought you would like a fast ride. You have a lot of spunk and fire, Miss Thompson."

"Please call me Florence. I didn't realize you are such a daredevil. You have a reputation for being very studious."

"I do? I didn't think many people paid much attention to my reputation. I'm not even here very often. I go to the Lutheran School over in Willmar. I was very homesick at first, especially after my mother died last year. But now I like it and I've made some great new friends."

They rode along in silence for a few minutes. Florence felt surprised about how open and straightforward Leonard was. Most Norwegians she knew rarely said a word about themselves or how they felt about much of anything. Most would never admit for a minute, to feeling homesick.

"What do you study at this school?" she asked.

"I like business law and accounting the best. I just know I don't want to be a farmer, although my father keeps trying to make one out of me. Lots of new opportunities are opening up in business these days. I just have to find the right niche, that's all."

He smiled directly at her in a way that melted her heart. She knew then and there, that he was the man she wanted. She felt certain that Leonard would make something of himself one day. But he was still in school and only seventeen. It could be a long, long time before Leonard could ever find that niche he was looking for. Just what that might be, she could not imagine.

Thoughts of the romantic ride in the cutter carried her through the next few weeks, and more coaching sessions with Ralph and Alta. After the big success of the Valentine spelling bee, Florence had talked them both into entering the county competition coming up in mid-March, to represent District 34 in both spelling and arithmetic. Florence felt her two star students were sure to win a prize.

The competition would be held at the courthouse in Benson on a Sunday afternoon, with a reception afterward in the lobby of the huge, turreted red brick building. Most of the school districts would be represented and parents from all over the county would attend. To enter the spelling competition meant facing the jaw-breaking words Miss Thorson might have on her list, and the superintendent was noted for finding the most obscure and difficult.

"I don't know why you want to work so hard," Ida said one weekend when they were together at Ida's boarding place. "Why did you want to enter those kids in the county competition? Don't you ever get sick of school?"

"I coach Ralph and Alta because I enjoy it," Florence said. "I'd rather spend my time with them than with Minnie and Carl. Any day." Florence always loved to get a laugh out of Ida, and to hear the latest details of Ida's budding romance with Rudolph Johnson. However, she kept quiet about her own interest in Leonard Kvam. After all, nothing might come of it. She hadn't seen him since the ride in the cutter.

On the day of the competition, Florence got a ride to Benson with Mr. and Mrs. Huston, who brought their entire family of eight. They found a place to sit in the back of the crowded courtroom, while Florence sat between Alta and Ralph in the reserved section in front. Alta seemed poised and looked very pretty in a blue dress with a white sash, her blond hair tied up with a blue ribbon. But Ralph looked the picture of agony.

"I didn't think the words would be *this* hard," he whispered, after seeing one contestant after another go down in defeat. "The Valentine program was easy, compared with this."

"We expected a lot of hard words, didn't we?" Florence squeezed his hand in reassurance. "Remember, all you have to do is your best. Nothing more."

At last, Miss Thorson called Ralph Huston from District 34. He looked at Florence with despair and marched up to his place in front of the judge's bench, in front of Miss Thorson who sat like a queen on a throne, dressed all in black, her faded blonde hair swept up in tight little waves.

"Grievous," said the superintendent, her voice booming out so everyone in the courtroom could hear.

Ralph spelled that word easily, remembering the rule about "i" before "e" except after "c". He mastered five more words, increasingly difficult, as the audience applauded each victory. Then Miss Thorson signaled for silence and looked at Ralph. This one was going to be a real killer, Florence knew. The last one was always the hardest.

"Pusillanimous." Miss Thorson pronounced each syllable, apparently proud to have discovered such an impossible word in her dictionary.

Florence groaned. This was a college level word intended to separate the brilliant spellers from those who were merely excellent. Florence wasn't sure she had even heard of the word before and put her trust in Ralph's grasp of phonics. He knew how to sound out the word to make the best possible guess.

The Valentine Program 127

The boy screwed up his face and looked at Florence. Then, in a slow deliberate way, he pronounced each letter, concentrating on the syllables. "P-U-S-I-L . . . L-A-N-I . . . M-O-U-S."

"That is absolutely correct!" A hint of a smile stole over Miss Thorson's face. It wasn't proper for a superintendent to have any favorites, but this was the first time a student from District 34 had entered a county competition in years.

A scattering of applause started from the back of the room, and then gained momentum. Facing the audience, Ralph bowed from his waist with his left hand pressed against his spine and his right hand covering the belt of his knickers, exactly the way Florence had taught him. She felt a burst of pride. Her star student had performed even better than she expected.

Alta did just as well in spelling, and even better in arithmetic. Anyone could see that District 34 was going to win a prize. When it was all over and the points were added up, Miss Thorson announced the winners.

"The First Place in spelling goes to Ralph Huston of District 34," said Miss Thorson. "This means that Ralph is eligible to go to Minneapolis for the state competition."

She went on to announce the other winners in each category. Florence felt as if she were floating on a cloud when Alta was called up to receive First Place in arithmetic and Ralph captured Second Place. It was too much to even dream about. Afterward, at the reception, Ida bustled up with a big smile on her face.

"This is a real feather in your cap, Florence. You must be mighty proud." Ida adjusted her spectacles, a sure sign of bad news to come. "But I don't envy you at all. Now you will have to coach those kids for the state competition. That will take up all your time."

"I know. I enjoy coaching them. I like competitions. I just wish I could afford to go to Minneapolis. But that's out of the question."

"You don't mean you would spend your hard-earned money on a train ticket and a hotel room just for a school competition! You are the limit, Florence."

"I would if I had the money," she said. "Guess what? Miss Thorson has decided to give a seminar in phonics this spring and not wait until fall. She's asked me to do a demonstration with my beginning readers."

"What! Do you mean you would get up in front of all those seasoned teachers? A rank beginner like you? Why, I'd be so nervous. Don't tell me you're going to do it."

"Of course I'm going to do it. It will be the first Saturday in April. My First Graders can hardly wait to show off all they have learned."

"Florence, well, I never. You are the absolute limit."

As usual, Ida was right. It was a big responsibility to coach Ralph and Alta every day after school, but Florence enjoyed every moment in a way she couldn't explain. There was something magical about seeing a student struggle with a dark barrier he couldn't comprehend. And then, after some explanations and examples, like a slowly dawning miracle, the student would grasp an entirely new concept; he would experience a burst of light when all became clear in his mind.

Florence went through the process many times with Ralph and Alta, trying this method and that, to make the miraculous light appear. While experimenting with different ways to reach a student, Florence learned more about teaching than she ever could have gleaned from a book.

Ralph and Alta went off to Minneapolis, primed to do their best at the state level. It didn't matter so much that they didn't come home with a prize. Ralph and Alta had been on the adventure of a lifetime, one they would always remember.

The last day of the term arrived at the end of March. There would be no spring term partly because of the empty treasury, and partly because it was planting season. Florence packed her trunk, feeling pity for the next teacher who would occupy this room and have to endure the grudging hospitality of Minnie and Carl. She hoped the next one would be able to speak Norwegian.

Leaning against the March wind, she ventured across the pasture for the last day of school, feeling an odd mixture of happiness and sadness. Did the children feel the same way, she wondered—happy to complete the term but sad to say a last farewell? When she reached the schoolyard, she couldn't help but notice mysterious bulges under some of the children's coats and the way they rushed up the steps and into the classroom the moment she unlocked the door. Something was up. She waited in the cloakroom for a few moments, listening to the hurried whispers and the scurry of activity. Then, when she opened the door, she saw a huge pile of gifts on her desk, wrapped in tissue paper and tied with ribbons.

"What a wonderful surprise!" Florence said. "I can't get over all this." She looked around at all the expectant faces, at Erik and Ingeborg and Harriet. And noticed one desk was vacant. "Where's Ralph?" she asked, feeling very let-down.

"He couldn't come today," Alta replied, tight-lipped. "He's home sick. That's all."

"Open the presents," the children called. "Open them. Open them."

Florence began to unwrap each gift, to hold up for everyone to see. There was a box of home-made fudge from Ingeborg's mother, an embroidered handkerchief from Alta Huston, a bottle of toilet water from Erik Togstaad, some little token of affection from each of her pupils.

The day progressed as usual and all the children came running to meet her when she returned from lunch. She held an extra-long story hour that afternoon and read the best-loved tales from *The Brothers Grimm* and tried to shrug off her disappointment. She hadn't imagined that Ralph would not be there to say a last goodbye. After the reading ended, she hugged each child in a last farewell. She dried the tears of the youngest ones, reminding them about the phonics seminar coming up in Benson, and how she expected them to do their very best. Then she watched her pupils scatter in all directions.

In the silence of the classroom, Florence began to tidy up for the last time. She checked to see the books were safely packaged so the mice would not get at them, and made sure the pail of water was emptied in case of a late spring freeze. It was time to go. There would be no last farewell with Ralph.

She turned to leave when suddenly, in the corner of her eye, she caught sight of a face at the window nearest her desk. She ran outside, thinking it might be Ralph, and called his name. No one answered. Florence thought it must have been her imagination playing tricks, and then she heard a muffled sob coming from around the corner of the schoolhouse.

"Is that you, Ralph?" she called. "Please come and say goodbye. I feel so disappointed, not to see you this one last time."

She walked around the corner and found him pressed against the wall, tears streaming down his face. He struggled to gain control of himself and finally was able to blurt out a few strangled words.

"G—Goodbye, Miss Thompson. I'll—I'll sure miss you." Ralph turned and ran as fast as his Fifth Grade legs could carry him, across the schoolyard, past the swings and into a clump of trees. He didn't look back but simply disappeared.

Swallowing back tears, Florence returned to the classroom to pick up the armful of gifts. She put on her coat and locked the schoolhouse door for the last time. Ida had warned her not to become too attached to her students, not to let herself be drawn into their lives. It wasn't right for a teacher to have favorites and the time always came when you had to say goodbye. And yet, how could she be a good teacher without caring about her students. How could that be possible? Where were the boundaries and how could she find them?

Back in her room a little later, she packed a few last minute things while waiting for Uncle Bernt to arrive. These past four months had been wonderful and dreadful. She felt glad to see the last of this barren room and the joyless Knudson family but it was hard to leave the children she had come to love. Now she looked forward to her appointment with Miss Thorson in a few days, to talk about a possible job for the spring term. She needed something to tide her over and help finance a summer session back at Moorhead. Life as a teacher was turning out to be a wonderful adventure—always with something new on the horizon. And now she would get to spend a few days at Grandmother's farm.

She heard the crunching sound of a horse and buggy in the driveway and the yapping bark of the Knudson's dog. Uncle Bernt! Florence picked up her valise and ran down the stairs to greet him.*

---

*In 1915, after two more years of in-fighting, the northwest section of District 34 split off and became a part of the new District 98. Note from the *History of Swift County,* pub. in 1979.

Florence when boarding at the Ronholdt farm, 1913

Chapter Seven

The Spring Creek School; District One

I need to warn you, Florence," Miss Thorson said during their interview, her brow wrinkled with worry as usual. "District 1 is a much bigger school than District 34. Thirty-four pupils are enrolled. Are you sure you can handle so many?"

"Of course I can." Florence didn't add that if she didn't get another teaching job on short notice, she couldn't afford to return to the Normal in June. Saving money was so terribly difficult.

"Are you sure about the thirty-four students?" Miss Thorson pressed. "The winter term just wore out Miss Bjorson. Then she took it in her head to just up and get married. That was the end of trying to talk her into finishing out the year."

Florence knew that was the end, all right. Marriage meant giving up teaching. "The rule about married women seems so unfair. Men teachers can get married and not have to quit their jobs."

Miss Thorson gave her a severe look. "Men don't get themselves in a family way, either. Everyone knows a woman can't show herself in public when she is expecting." So far as the superintendent was concerned, that settled the matter.

"It still doesn't seem fair. But I'm happy to have the job and now I will be closer to my grandmother's farm. That will be just wonderful."

"I'm sure you will like this boarding place at the Ronholdt's. They are such a nice family and you should feel quite to home there."

The interview ended on a cheerful note although Florence couldn't shake off the feeling she was profiting at someone else's expense. If women could ever get the vote, then teachers would have more say about these stupid rules. However, for as long as she could remember, the suffragettes had been marching and pleading for their rights. And getting nowhere. Men continued to ridicule the "girls in bloomers" every chance they could, even though most suffragettes didn't wear bloomers at all but regular clothes like everyone else. She hoped to live long enough to actually cast a vote someday.

Florence found herself in a different world at the Ronholdt farm. Now she had a pleasant upstairs room with a rug on the floor and pictures on the walls plus the usual bureau and an oak table that would be perfect for correcting papers. Mrs. Ronholdt greeted her with outstretched arms and Ole, her husband, seemed equally pleased to board the teacher. Best of all, the Ronholdt daughters were close to her own age—dark-haired Julia who was twenty-two, and Ovidia who was just eighteen. After the dreary Knudson place, the Ronholdt farm seemed too good to be true.

However, the school turned out to be everything Miss Thorson had predicted, and worse. The thirty-four students were spread through all the grade levels, so there was no chance to merge two or three grades together for any of the subjects. Just keeping order was the biggest challenge and on the first day, Florence tottered home with a violent headache.

"Are you feeling sick?" Ovidia asked when she found Florence in the kitchen, making a cup of tea. "You look dreadful." Ovidia was an energetic young woman, with a round puckish face and a figure that some people might call "pleasingly plump."

"I'm just worn out and worried," Florence replied. "I don't know how I'm going to manage this school. I'll have to ask a couple of the older girls to help with the beginning readers. What I need is a full-time assistant. My head is splitting and I'm going up to my room to lie down."

Ovidia made a cold compress with a cloth and some icy well water, and followed Florence upstairs. "There now, you just relax and let me put this on your forehead. I hope you and I are going to be good friends. It's so lonely out here on the farm. Do you know what I like to do best? Just to amuse myself?"

"I have no idea." The cold cloth felt good on her throbbing head and Florence stretched out on the bed and closed her eyes, hoping Ovidia would take the hint and leave.

"My favorite thing," Ovidia continued, "just to break the monotony around here, is getting my picture taken at the photographer's studio in Benson. It's fun to strike a pose and pretend I'm a model for the Montgomery Ward catalogue. Would you like to do that with me sometime?"

"Maybe. Sometime." Florence rarely had been to a photographer. There was her confimation picture, of course, and then she had posed for a few personalized picture postcards that were so in vogue. Her sisters loved receiving them. But she never had thought of a photographer's studio as a place of entertainment. She sighed, not wanting to hurt Ovidia's feelings. "Right now, I'd like to rest."

For the balance of the week, Florence coped with the constant confusion in the classroom and every day when she arrived home, Ovidia was waiting with a cold compress and a cup of hot tea. She begged and cajoled about going to the photographer's. At the end of the week, after all these ministrations, Florence relented.

On Saturday, she put on her best dress, the lacy one she had worn for recitals at Moorhead, and Ovidia donned her black bombazine, a twilled and worsted silk, the type of fabric intended to last for years and years. Julia decided on a gray taffeta with a bodice buttoned up to her neck and a full skirt that touched the floor. Mr. Ronholdt agreed to take them to town, since he needed to market the eggs anyway.

He dropped them off at the studio on Main Street, which turned out to be a place of enchantment, with its choice of dainty pastel backdrops of endearing bucolic scenes, and its collection of mandarin chairs and elegant settees done up in lacy rattan. For one portrait, Florence

Ovidia & Julia Rondholdt, 1913

posed with an armless stool-like chair in mahogany with
an intricately carved high Victorian backrest. The possibilities for glamour were endless. The girls arranged themselves in pensive poses, while Florence watched the pro-

prietor set up his big boxy Kodak on a tripod and then huddle under the black cloth canopy to peer into the lens. "Hold still," he shouted, before setting off the blinding flash.

It was hard to hold a pose like a statue, not daring to breathe, while the proprietor counted off the minutes for the image to impress itself on this mysterious glass-like film. As a result, when they returned the next week to see the finished product, the expressions on their faces looked somber and not like themselves at all. But the trips to the studio were fun and diverting and before the spring term ended, Florence had a picture of herself in just about every outfit in her wardrobe, and using every prop and background scene available. The photographer liked these pictures so much, he gave the girls a discount and displayed some of the portraits in his front window.

During these brief weeks of the spring term, bouncy Ovidia loved to ply Florence with questions about life and love. One favorite game was a quiz about available bachelors who might make suitable husbands. She composed a narrow list of possibilities, to be recited while Florence was prone on her bed with a cold compress on her throbbing head. The turmoil at school was not getting any better.

"Now Florence. . .here's an idea. How about Nels Fingerson? He's a bachelor."

Nels was treasurer of the school board and owned the neighboring farm. Every two weeks, Florence walked over there to collect her paycheck and Ovidia couldn't hear enough about these visits. Nels always made a great ceremony of opening his big wooden roll-top desk to reveal pigeonholes stuffed with important-looking papers. Then he would open his big leather-bound checkbook the size of a photo album, and lay it flat on the desk. With precision, he would dip the nub of his long quill pen into the inkwell and then shake off a drop or two, before making out the check in his thin spidery handwriting. He wrote in the looping backhand style used by court clerks and ministers, and then he would blow on the check to make sure the ink was dry. With a dignified but thin-lipped smile, he would hand it over to Florence. Mr. Fingerson never had a check made out ahead of time. He always went through this elaborate routine.

"Nels Fingerson!" Florence lifted a corner of her cold compress to stare at Ovidia in mock horror. "Now you are at the bottom of the barrel. Nels Fingerson is forty years old, if he's a day. He lives with his mother for goodness sake. If I married him, I'd have to put up with *her.* Can't you think of a better prospect than that?" Of course, Florence didn't say a word about her interest in Leonard Kvam. If Ovidia knew about him, there would be no end to the teasing.

"Well, Nels may be old but he has a nice house. How about Augaton Jorgenson? He has a house and a motorcar. You could marry him."

"Augaton is sweet on Ida. Let's cross him off the list."

"Let's pretend you had to choose, as if your life depended on it. Which one would it be? Nels or Augaton?"

Florence groaned. Ovidia was insatiable. When she wasn't talking about prospective husbands, she wanted to know every detail of Florence private life and her financial independence. Florence was in a position to spend her money any way she pleased without anyone, especially not a father, to lay down the law. Then a mysterious package arrived at the house, and Ovidia was beside herself with excitement.

"Florence! Florence!" she called from the foot of the stairs. "Come down right away. Father picked up a big packing box for you at the post office. I'll die if you don't come down and open it right this minute!"

Florence arose from her late afternoon nap with a start. She knew exactly what was in the package. She had spent five of her precious dollars to have a taffeta dress made in Fargo, something special to wear to programs and dances.

"I've been waiting for this," Florence declared a few minutes later, as she removed the packing tissue from a blue dress with yards and yards of fabric. She held it up to her shoulders, to show her dazzled friend. "Emily Beckstrom, my dressmaker, made it for me."

"Your dressmaker!" Ovidia sighed with envy. Ovidia had to make her own clothes, as did Julia and their mother. The foot pedal sewing machine was always humming in the sewing room, which was stocked with pattern books and a long table for cutting out fabric.

"I was beginning to think the dress would never come," Florence continued. "I sent Emily the money right after I got my first paycheck way last December, but Emily can be very unreliable. She doesn't always complete a dress when she promises. I put up with that because Emily has such divine ideas. She knows all about the latest fashions."

Ovidia's gaze took in the dark blue taffeta dress with a rounded neckline, lace on the bodice, the nipped in waist, with a hemline an inch shorter than any dress Ovidia had ever seen. "How did you ever find such a wonderful dress-maker?"

"I owe it all to my sister, Bernice. She works at the Economy Drugstore in Fargo, right across the river from Moorhead. Emily was a customer at the drugstore and she told me later, she couldn't help but notice the way Bernice dressed. She didn't know the first thing about fashion. My sister used to dress so terribly before she met Emily."

"Emily just. . .made her over?" Ovidia was enthralled.

"Exactly. The two became good friends. Then Emily invited Bernice to be her roommate, and share her rented room above a grocery store and cut expenses. That worked out just fine for Bernice, since Mother was about to move from Fargo out to Rhame, North Dakota, and Bernice certainly didn't want to live in such a wilderness. I have a sister and two brothers homesteading out there."

"How lucky for Bernice and Emily. To live in a big city like Fargo."

"Emily sews for the best people in town but I will say, she puts on airs. She thinks her name is too Swedish and wants to change it. Imagine that."

Florence went on to tell about the ups and downs of their fortunes, while she was in school at Moorhead; about the good times the three of them had just to go window-shopping without so much as a dime in their purses.

"How does Emily manage to fit you so perfectly," Ovidia asked, once Florence had put on the dress and whirled around to show it off.

"Bernice is exactly my size except she's an inch short-er. So Emily can try things on Bernice. And Bernice can go along with Emily to the dry goods store, to make sure Emily doesn't try to cheat me on the cost of the fabric."

"You have such a wonderful life," sighed Ovidia. "Making money of your own. I'd give anything to be you."

Florence felt touched by all this undue admiration. Fifty dollars a month wasn't much to show for all the work she put in at school, but she didn't need to account to anyone. Country teaching wasn't an easy way to earn a living, but Florence wouldn't have traded places with anyone.

The spring term ended and it was time to pack her trunk again. Florence felt she hadn't made much progress with her pupils. There were just too many, and not enough time to get to know any of them very well. But with the help of some of the older girls, she had managed to keep discipline and order. That was an accomplishment in itself. But now it was time to say goodbye to Ovidia and the Ronholdts. Amid tears and promises to write, she boarded the train for Moorhead.

It felt good to be back at Wheeler Hall and once settled in her room, Florence went to see her new advisor about the matter of her First Class Certificate. This had been troubling her and she thought there must be a way to satisfy the requirements in the shortest possible time. Getting a First Class Certificate would mean a raise in pay. As soon as she entered the advisor's office, Florence got right to the point.

"I'd like to talk with you about my schedule this summer," she said to the young man seated behind his desk.

He looked just barely out of college, clean-shaven like most of the younger men these days, and he was dressed in the worst possible choice for a warm June day, in a dark worsted suit with a high, starched shirt collar.

"You have seen the list of subjects you must take this summer," he said. "Do you have a question about that?"

"Yes, I do. I see that algebra is on my list and I find that very distressing. To take that course would be such a waste of time. I've always kept up with my algebra. I could pass the exam right now. I need so many other subjects. Like Civics and American history. Why can't I take one of those instead?"

"You must follow the requirements like everyone else, Miss Thompson." He looked irritated by her impertinence.

"Then I shall go to see Dean Hollis," she said. "He might listen to my problem. All I want is to take the algebra exam now and get the credit. I'm not the first student here to be short of money, and I can't waste mine on a subject I already know."

The advisor rolled his eyes heavenward. "Suit yourself, Miss Thompson. But I can assure you that Dean Hollis never has heard of such a thing."

That evening, Florence confided her mission to three of her friends at Wheeler Hall. "How do you have the nerve to see the Dean?" one of them asked. "Aren't you scared?" asked another.

"I have the nerve and I'm not scared," Florence declared. "Come with me tomorrow and you'll see that it pays to ask for what you want. The Dean can't do anything more than say no."

The next day, the three friends hovered outside the door of the Dean's office, waiting to hear the verdict. When Florence emerged, all smiles, they pelted her with questions.

"What did he say?" they asked, looking breathless. None of them ever had tried to change a requirement before.

"It was so simple," Florence said. "The Dean thought it was a good idea for me to take the exam now and see if I can pass. He was impressed because I think I'm good enough in algebra to be able to do it. Just maybe, sometime in the future, he will let other students do the same thing."

The aspiring teachers fluttered around Florence like vaudeville fans at the stage door, expressing amazement that she would dare to confront the Dean. All the fuss made Florence feel a little uncomfortable.

Later, when she had more time to think about it, she realized the real problem was with her friends, not with the requirements or even advisors with a rigid attitude. These girls had no experience in speaking up for themselves. They never had questioned the authority of men, whereas she had been making her own way for years now. While Florence missed not having a father, she realized her fate was not such a bad one after all. She was used to depending upon herself.

Florence passed the algebra exam and got the credit. At the end of the summer session, she was faced with the same old problem. No money. She had passed all her exams but she had just enough in her purse to pay for a train ticket back to Benson. The First Class Certificate would have to wait until the following summer, and the only solution was to write to Miss Thorson to ask about a job.

A few days later, she received a letter from the superintendent filled with pros and cons. The Holloway School in Edison Township was open and if she wanted the job, she would have to be there by Labor Day. Thirty children were enrolled and they enjoyed a reputation for good deportment. However, the boarding place at the Pederson farm was a fair distance away. Four miles by road but there was a short cut through a patch of woods.

The big problem was Mr. Pederson. None of the boarding teachers had a good word to say for him and most said he had the manners of an ox. Worse yet, the Pederson place didn't have a telephone. But there might be a small raise in pay, if things worked out. Did she want to accept the position?

Did she? It didn't take long for Florence to make up her mind. She sat down that instant to dash off a letter to Miss Thorson. She would be most pleased to take the position at Holloway. She added that it would be very nice if the fearsome Mr. Pederson could plan to meet her train.

Chapter Eight
The Holloway School;
District 69

On Labor Day, early in the afternoon, Florence sat in the dusty passenger car of the Great Northern Railroad, fretting over how late the train would be. It had been an hour late leaving Fargo and now a heavy rain had begun, pelting huge drops against her window while the train crept at a tortoise pace, falling farther and farther behind schedule. It would be at least another hour before she arrived at the depot in Benson. From there, she would need to change to a spur line called the "dinky" by the local people. That meant another half-hour ride to her final destination. She could just imagine how frustrated Mr. Pederson would be by now, with all this delay.

Once again, she took the letter from Ida out of her purse, to re-read the exciting news. Wonder of wonders— Ida was now officially engaged to Rudolph Johnson. They would have a simple ceremony and she wanted Florence to be her only attendant. A bridesmaid for the first time in her life! No date had been set because there were so many obstacles. For one thing, Ida had signed the contract to teach again at District 88 this fall and for another,

Merchant's Hotel

Rudolph didn't want to wait until next June. He wanted to get married in a few months, as soon as he found a suitable house in Benson. The idea of a winter wedding distressed Ida no end. No sensible person in Minnesota would do that, since the churches were unheated and the roads would be covered with snow. Ida was in a quandary and she and Rudolph were at loggerheads.

Florence folded the letter and put it back in her purse. How typical of Ida to worry about her contract when now she could have what she always had wanted—a husband and a house of her own in town. She felt sure that Ida and Rudolph could work it out in their own way. The exciting part was in becoming a bridesmaid. She could hardly wait to consult with Ida about what to wear.

At last the Great Northern pulled into Benson and Florence dashed into the depot, only to discover there

The Great Northern Depot at Holloway

would be another half-hour wait for the dinky, a three-car freight with one passenger car that served the tiny hamlet of Holloway. Florence supervised the transfer of her trunk and dreaded the worst. Since the Pederson family didn't have a telephone, there was no way to call and warn her future landlord that she would be late.

The rain continued to fall in buckets when Florence finally arrived at the tiny wooden depot, and she could see her worst fears had been confirmed. There stood a stocky farmer dressed in soaking wet overalls and jacket, looking as if he were about to explode. Water ran down in rivulets from his thatch of dark hair, over his jutting dark brow and grimly-set jaw.

"That yours?" he asked with a jerk of his head toward the trunk being wheeled in by the stationmaster.

"Yes, it is. I'm the new teacher. Miss Thompson. You must be Mr. Pederson. I'm sorry the train is so late."

He picked up the trunk and resting it on one brawny shoulder, he stomped toward the door and out to the platform. Florence followed. Once outside in the downpour, he shoved the trunk into the back of his carriage, leaving Florence to pick her way through the mud to the passenger side, to slide under the protection of the buggy hood.

"I was to home and back twice," Pederson growled. "Four miles. Waiting for you."

"The train was late. There wasn't a thing I could do about that." She didn't add that his lack of a telephone wasn't her fault either.

As the horse started to trot down the main street, Florence caught a glimpse of Merchant's Hotel, a two-storied wooden building across from the depot. This was the hotel Ida had told her about, a favorite weekend gathering place for local teachers. This gave Florence a ray of hope as she listened to the steady stream of rain on the buggy hood and the squishing of wooden wheels on the muddy road. But it would be two weeks before she could collect her first paycheck and have any chance to visit this haven of refuge.

At last the horse turned into a rutted lane and they drove past a huge barn and a summer shanty used for cooking and laundry. The carriage pulled to a stop near the kitchen porch of a tiny, two-storied house. Suddenly, in a storm of barking and snarling, two huge dogs streaked from the barn. They were about the size of boxers and they looked so ferocious, Florence screamed in alarm.

"Down, Devil. Down Satan," Mr. Pederson commanded in a loud voice. Instantly, the dogs obeyed and slunk back toward the barn.

"Why do you keep such brutes?" Florence asked. "They would scare the life out of anyone."

"Devil and Satan won't hurt you," Pederson said. "They will get used to having you around. I keep them to scare off the tramps around here. Maybe you noticed the vacant house we passed by on the road. It's a regular hang-out for hobos."

Still unnerved by the dogs, Florence grabbed her valise and hurried through the rain to the kitchen porch. Pederson followed with the trunk and then he led the horse to the barn. A small, dark-haired woman opened the door and peeked out.

"Land sakes, come on in," she said. "You'll catch your death out there." She wore a plain housedress with an apron tied around her middle. She had pinched little face and tiny blue-gray eyes that seemed to dart in every direction, as if she had a nervous tic.

"Hello. I'm Miss Thompson," Florence said as she hurried into the room and took off her wet jacket and hat. It was the usual kind of farm kitchen with a wood range, a tall cupboard for the dishes and a metal sink with a hand pump. The table was set for supper and the smell of beef stew filled the air. Two little girls hung behind their mother, faces aglow with curiosity.

"I'm Emma Pederson and this little girl is Vivian. She's in the Second Grade now. And this is Dorothy. She's in the Sixth."

"I'm very pleased to meet you and so sorry I've held up your supper. The train was terribly late. Would you show me the way to school tomorrow, Dorothy? I've heard there is a short cut."

"We're not going to school tomorrow," Dorothy declared. "We're going to the fair."

"The county fair over to Appleton," Emma Pederson explained. "It's the biggest thing that happens around here all year. Most everybody goes. I expect you won't have many children in school tomorrow."

"How strange. I wonder why the school board doesn't postpone the opening of school, until the fair is over." As she hung her wet jacket on a peg near the door, she could sense something very peculiar about this family. A sort of nervous tension seemed to hang in the air.

"The coffee is hot. Let's have a cup before my husband gets back." Emma's glance darted about the kitchen, to the table and then back to the kitchen door. Her hands trembled a little as she reached for the porcelain cups. "Your room is downstairs here, Miss Thompson. Just off the parlor. We're upstairs, with the girls."

Florence heard another din of barking and another loud command from Mr. Pederson coming from the direction of the kitchen porch. The shy smiles faded from the faces of Vivian and Dorothy and Emma almost dropped the porcelain cup. The door flew open and Mr. Pederson shoved the trunk across the kitchen floor, leaving a trail of wet dirt. Then he picked up the trunk with heaving grunt and dropped it with a thud in the next room.

"Let me get a rag and wipe up the floor," Florence offered.

"Oh, no. I'll do it." Quick as a flash, Emma scurried to a box in the corner, found a towel and got down on her hands and knees to wipe up the tracks. Mr. Pederson clumped back into the kitchen, leaving another trail of dirt. He picked up a book from the table and carried it into the parlor.

Emma gave Florence an apologetic smile, the coffee

forgotten. "You go ahead and unpack, Miss Thompson. Dorothy can help you. I'll finish up supper."

Dorothy led the way to Florence's room, carefully skirting her father's booted feet outstretched on a hassock as he sat absorbed in the book, a look of exasperation on his face. The bedroom designated for the teacher was so tiny there was just enough space for the iron bedstead and a small bureau. The only window overlooked the back yard. Across one corner hung a calico curtain, to make a closet area. There was no table for correcting papers and Florence feared that would have to be done in the parlor under Pederson's watchful glare.

"The room isn't very big, is it," Dorothy asked, wrinkling her nose. "We have bigger rooms upstairs, but the teachers always say it's more private down here. Do you like to be private, Miss Thompson?"

"Yes. Yes, I do. This room will be just fine."

All through supper Mr. Pederson sat like a smoldering volcano while Emma tried to carry on a conversation, asking the usual polite questions about her teaching background. Florence helped with the dishes and afterward, when she was in her nightgown and ready for bed, she heard a gentle tap, tap on her bedroom door. Emma scurried in, carrying a tray with a mug of hot cocoa and a little plate of cookies.

"This isn't much of a welcome, Miss Thompson. Please don't mind my husband. He's in one of his moods again. It will pass." She put the tray on the bureau with a nervous smile.

"It's all right. I understand, Mrs. Pederson. And please call me Florence. I hope you and I can be good friends."

"Oh, I hope so, too." Emma glanced at the door as if she were afraid someone might hear. "Now you eat the cookies. Oatmeal and raisin. The girls love them. And please call me Emma."

"Thank you. But you really didn't need to do this."

"Yes, I did. Harold was so ugly to you. But it's just a mood. He gets into moods like this. It isn't just that your train was so late, and then being caught in the rain. But this will pass." She slipped out of the room before Florence could protest again.

The next morning was bright and sunny, and the Pederson family set off for Appleton, the biggest town in the area, to attend the fair. After receiving directions from Dorothy, Florence found the shortcut to school, through a patch of woods and a neighbor's pasture. The place looked like a dream castle compared with her two previous schools. The playground equipment was in good repair and the schoolhouse looked freshly painted. There was a squat bell tower with a bell that actually worked. All the books looked fresh and new and were neatly arranged on the shelves. The classroom and the cloakroom were spanking clean. Florence could hardly believe her good fortune.

Only nine children turned up that first day and when they told Florence the fair would last an entire week, she felt puzzled and disappointed. Again, she wondered why the school board hadn't postponed the opening of school and at noon, she decided to make an announcement.

"Children, I don't see much use in letting you get so far ahead of the others. Let's dismiss for today. I will see you tomorrow."

Florence picked up a few books to carry home and started off on the short-cut path. She thought perhaps Mr. Pederson would be in a better mood after a day at the fair. He had been cross as a bear at breakfast. But at least now she would have lots of time to read and get ahead on some lessons, since the family would not be back until late afternoon. Lost in thought, Florence opened the gate in the fence and approached the house. Then she saw the two huge dogs asleep on the kitchen porch, and started to go around to the front door. One dog raised his head, spotted her in the yard and raced in her direction, snarling and showing his fangs. The other one was right behind him, yapping and growling. Florence screamed, dropped the books, and ran toward the safety of the summer shanty. The dogs were right at her heels and just in time, she yanked open the door and slammed it behind her.

After catching her breath, Florence surveyed her little prison. A dim light filtered down from the bank of high windows to reveal the wood stove, a worktable covered with an oilcloth, and a metal laundry tub set up on legs near a metal sink. There was one straight-back chair and Florence climbed up on that, to peer outside. The dogs were quiet now, out of sight, but she could see her books on the ground, tantalizing close but so unreachable. A half hour passed in silence while she tried to think of some way to sneak out and grab the books, without awakening the dogs. It was long past lunchtime and her stomach started to grumble. She peeked out the door, hoping the wretched dogs might be back in the barn but they were on the porch again, fast asleep.

She decided, ever so quietly, to tiptoe over to the books and try to slip around to the front of the house. She took a tentative step outside, then two, then three and in a flash, the dogs awoke and were at her heels again, barking and snarling. Florence retreated to the cook shanty and slammed the door.

There was nothing to do but wait for the Pederson's return. Three long tiresome hours passed. Every time she looked out the door, she saw the dogs still on the porch. She thought she would go mad from boredom, cooped up this way and helpless. Then at long last, she heard the clip-clop of horse's hooves and the crunch of buggy wheels. The dogs set up a ferocious din until they were silenced by one harsh command. Florence dashed out of the shanty. "Thank God you're home! Those dogs kept me penned up for hours!"

Harold Pederson stood next to the buggy, arms akimbo. He threw his head back in uproarious laughter, as if he never had seen anything so funny in his entire life, while Emma and the girls sat in the buggy and stared. Florence knew she must look a sight with stains of sweat on her dress and her hair rumpled, but she failed to see any humor in this.

"I could have been killed," she shouted. "And you think this is funny?"

Pederson stopped laughing. "I told you before these dogs won't hurt you. They're not anywhere near as ferocious as they look. So the big important teacher didn't know enough to listen to me."

Florence glared in his direction. If looks could kill, that would have been the end of Harold Pederson. He would have been sprawled stone cold dead on the ground.

Florence walked over to her books, picked them up and marched into the house. If it had been possible, she would have moved that instant to some other boarding place. But such a thing wasn't possible. There was no choice but to remain at the Pederson farm and make the best of it.

A little later, feeling faint from hunger, she joined the family for supper. As usual, Emma bustled back and forth, seeing to her husband's every need, while Dorothy and Vivian watched in painful silence. Florence thought about payday a week from Friday. Once she got her hands on some money, she could flee for the weekend to the sanctuary of the Merchant's Hotel.

That evening, after the dishes were done, Florence heard a faint tap, tap, tap on her bedroom door. Emma came in with tray of hot cocoa and cookies. "I'm so sorry, Florence. Harold didn't mean to laugh at you. He didn't realize how scared you were. Please forgive him."

"Thank you, Emma. It's sweet of you to bring a tray, but this really isn't necessary. I can't promise to forgive him. I'm not even sure it's possible for me to forgive him. But I promise you I will try."

Emma gave Florence a nervous smile and gently closed the door. The last thing Florence wanted was another peace offering. Nothing could make up for the humiliation of that day and still she felt a surge of compassion for Emma. In her heart of hearts, Florence knew that men like Harold Pederson found some wicked pleasure in acting so spiteful. Even frightened Emma must have realized that perverse side of his nature. So what did forgiveness have to do with it? Harold Pederson didn't show much sign of ever changing It was a conundrum that Florence couldn't comprehend but for Emma's sake, and for her own, she tried to put the problem out of her mind.

Vivian and Dorothy laughed and skipped on their way to school with Florence the next morning. They were like different children when they were away from home, full of fun and carefree. However, the first week of school turned out to be disappointing and unproductive, because most of the other pupils continued to attend the fair every day. She dreaded the weekend that would bring only more boorish behavior from Harold Pederson and more placating from Emma. On Saturday and Sunday, she stayed in her room and read and re-read all the lessons for the coming week.

The following Monday, all the children were in attendance and Florence settled into her new routine. This class size of thirty was much easier than District 1, and there were moments when Florence felt almost sorry for the town teachers. They had to teach the same grade, year after year. In her country school, she could teach every grade and some new challenge came along almost every day.

Friday arrived at last and Florence packed her valise. She planned to go straight from school to the Merchant's Hotel. She only needed to stop at the treasurer's farm on the way, to pick up her paycheck. She dismissed class a little early and walked to town, for her first look at the tiny hamlet of Holloway nestled along the railroad track. The hotel, across from the depot, was a wood frame structure with a wide, second-floor balcony supported by four sturdy pillars. Much bigger than it looked from the street, the hotel was twice as deep as it was wide, and could boast of having fifteen rooms. Filled with anticipation, Florence entered the foyer to ask the price of a room.

"That will be thirty-five cents, dear. In advance." Mrs. Severson, the large-bosomed proprietor, smiled from behind the polished wood reception desk in the main parlor, a place decorated with gas lamps, stiff Victorian furniture and a faded Persian rug on the floor. In one corner, Florence noticed an upright piano littered with sheet music, complete with a round swivel stool that could be adjusted for various heights.

"I'm the new teacher at District 69," Florence said. "I've heard that other teachers in the area like to come here, too. I'm eager to meet them."

"Oh, yes. We're like one happy family here. The girls usually turn up before six o'clock suppertime. It's home style and I do my own cooking."

After cashing Florence's paycheck, Mrs. Severson led the way upstairs, to a small room near the back with a dormer window. It had all the usual amenities, an iron bedstead covered with a light woolen blanket, a heavy bureau and a wash stand, with the extra luxury of a tall, brown metal gas heater.

"The bath tub is in a separate room down the hall and the privy is down the basement," the hotelkeeper explained. "Or you can use the slop jar that's under the bed, and take it down there yourself."

"Thank you. This is a lovely room."

Florence couldn't have been happier and she met five local teachers at supper. They chatted about the latest political problems in the country, and in particular about President Wilson's trouble with Mexico where a civil war was brewing. Of still more interest was the rumor that Lillie Thorson might have some competition for her position as superintendent. But the election was still a year away.

"Pooh," said Bessie Jorgenson, a plump blonde young woman seated at the table. "I don't care who wins the election. It won't make any difference in my paycheck."

"That's all Bessie thinks about," whispered a pretty teacher sitting next to Florence, as they finished a dessert of strawberries and cream. "Her paycheck. I'll bet that Bessie never bothers to read the postings we get from the state on topics for civics class. Or even the newspapers. I eat that up, myself. Reading about the outside world makes me feel less isolated. By the way, my name is Petra Hamre. What's yours?"

Before Florence could answer, everyone started to beg Petra to play the piano. The young women moved to the parlor to gather around the upright. It felt so delightful to be with young people again, almost like being back at Wheeler Hall. Florence volunteered to teach her new friends some songs she had learned that summer and for a while, the turmoil in the nation's capitol and the dark cloud at the Pederson farm, drifted far from her mind.

"Do go shopping with us, Florence," Petra Hamre said the next morning at breakfast. "Some of us are going to take the dinky to Benson."

"I can't afford to buy anything just now, but I'll go with you to Benson. I want to visit my aunt's boarding place. I haven't seen her all summer."

Florence checked out of the hotel and brought her valise, knowing she could spend the night with Ida at the H. R. Hanson farm. She wanted to catch up on the latest wedding news. Once in town, she stopped at the Olson Hardware store to see about getting a ride out to the farm with Rudolph.

"I don't know why Ida is so hesitant about getting married right away," Rudolph grumbled, once they were on the road in his buggy. "She listens to everyone else when we certainly are old enough to make up our own minds."

Florence laughed. They certainly were old enough. Almost thirty. "You know how practical Ida is. She's worried about the idea of a winter wedding."

"I'm practical too. I just bought a house in Benson. It's on a big corner lot and it has four bedrooms and a stable. When Ida sees it, she'll be so pleased. I'm sure she'll change her mind."

"Did you buy a house without Ida seeing it first?"

"Why not?" Rudolph couldn't hide the twinkle in his eye. "I know how to handle Ida. I bought a wedding ring, too. I'm ready to get married and I'm going to talk Ida into tying the knot by Christmas."

Florence could see he was a very determined man and it looked like he would win out in the end.

"Well, I never," Ida announced after hearing about the purchase of a house. She put down the tray of coffee she was serving in the parlor and looked at Rudolph and then at Florence, an expression of amazement on her face.

"You actually bought a house! I think you're rushing things," Ida said. "You know I can't just walk out on my contract. The fall term already has started."

"The term will be over in December," Rudolph insisted. "If you give notice right now, Miss Thorson can find another teacher to finish up the year."

"Here we go again, with talk about a winter wedding," Ida replied with a fleeting and slightly desperate look at Florence. "People just don't get married in the winter."

"We're not like most people. And I'm not going to live alone in that big house. I bought it for you and we are going to live there as soon as possible. Don't you want a house of your own in town?"

Florence could see that Ida was beginning to weaken. That had been her dream and now it could come true.

"Well," Ida said, "if it has to be winter, I insist on one thing. That we have the reception at my mother's house. If we don't, she will be very hurt." Ida adjusted her spectacles, determined to win this one point.

"What about Christmastime?" Rudolph pressed.

"Well, maybe a week later," Ida said. "We could have a small private ceremony in Benson. We both have plenty of relatives there, goodness knows. But the reception will have to be at Mother's farm."

A smile spread over Rudolph's face. He had won his point about a winter wedding, frozen roads or not. "I'll ask my cousin, Robert Hanson. He and Jenny have a nice big house with an organ. You could ask Bernice to play."

Ida sat back in her chair, arms folded and trying to look stern, but with a look of love on her face. "Well, I feel guilty about breaking my contract. But since you can't wait until June. . .well. . .we can settle on early January."

"The day after New Year's," Rudolph said. "How's that?"

"All right, then. January 2nd it is," Ida agreed.

Florence felt a twinge of envy. Ida had a man so eager to marry her that he couldn't wait until spring. And she, herself, had no prospects at all.

"I still feel leery about a winter wedding," Ida said later that night, as she and Florence were getting ready for bed. "We could be snowed in. And it's a long trip out to Mother's place. About thirty-five miles. What if we can't get there?"

"If there is snow, we can go by sled," Florence replied. "That would be fun. And so romantic. I can't wait to hear what Grandma Betsy has to say about all this."

Ida laughed. "I think Mother had given up on my getting married at all. It's a good thing she likes Rudolph and approves of the match. I hope Bernice can come all the way from Fargo."

"Oh, she'll come, I'm sure." Florence snuggled under the quilt in the beautiful bedroom reserved for the boarding teacher. Life seemed so unbearably good. Ida and Rudolph were happy; everyone was pleased with the match; she had found new friends at the Merchant's Hotel. Best of all, Emily would have plenty of time to make the bridesmaid dress and Bernice could bring it from Fargo. The only worry now was finding the proper design for a January bridesmaid.

Directly after church on Sunday, Florence placed a call to the depot in Benson, to find out what time the dinky would be in.

"Oh dear. Not until then?" She turned to Ida. "The train won't leave until five o'clock. That's really late. I guess you'll be stuck with me for the afternoon."

"Don't look so worried. Rudolph is coming back to talk some more about the wedding. He can take you to the depot."

"What worries me is Mr. Pederson. He gets so upset if I'm late for supper. And I don't like the idea of walking back there after dark. I've heard there are some tramps living on that road."

After Rudolph dropped her at the station, Florence learned the dinky would be delayed again and she would have to wait another hour. Some of the local teachers drifted in to catch the train and when the dinky finally arrived, they all boarded. After the half-hour trip, the young women scattered in several directions, heading for their own boarding places.

Now Florence cast a fearful look at the darkening sky. With valise in hand, she started out on the road. The sun hung low on the horizon, casting its last rays over the stubble in the surrounding cornfields. She tried not to dwell on her few experiences with tramps. She had seen them hanging from freight cars and just the week before, she had seen evidence of their presence in her school yard—the remains of a camp fire, scraps of food, an empty whiskey bottle. She never had met a tramp face to face, and hoped never to meet one.

She counted the fence posts along the way to keep her mind occupied, knowing she would soon have to pass that spooky vacant house. The place looked ominous even in daylight, with its round cupola jutting out from the collapsing roof, leaving a hole that opened to the sky. A forest of weeds climbed up the walls and the jagged edges of the broken windows looked like the crooked teeth of a jack o' lantern. Now, as the abandoned house came into view, Florence shivered. She walked a little faster, shifting the valise from one hand to the other. She could feel her heart beating a little more rapidly as she drew closer to the eerie house, shrouded now in shadows. She saw no sign of anyone about. Her step quickened. Then she heard a strange flapping sound . . . flap . . . flap . . . flap . . . like sheets hung out to dry in a strong wind. But there was no wind, just a light breeze, and there was no clothesline in sight.

She walked faster. Then, to her horror, she saw the figure of a man on the road, weaving and stumbling along a few yards ahead of her. In the deepening twilight, she could see that he wore a dark jacket that was much too big for him, and it flapped against his lean and sinewy frame as he staggered along. Not wanting to overtake him on the road, Florence slowed her pace. Then suddenly, he turned around to peer at her as if surprised that someone was following. He loped back toward her, arms waving, jacket flapping. "Hey!" he called.

The quickening drum in Florence's breast beat faster. What could she do to defend herself on this deserted road? Before she had time to think, the man was next to her, up close, staring at her with bloodshot eyes, the smell of whiskey on his breath. He stood half a foot taller than she, with matted gray hair sticking out in all directions, squint lines around his narrow eyes, stubby gray whiskers on his chin. "Hey!" he shouted again.

"Please let me pass," Florence said and took a step to one side. He minced forward to block her way.

"Hey!" he repeated. "Hey, you girl!"

She edged to the other side of the road. He blocked her way again and leaned down to stare in her face. Florence thought she would faint from the terrible smell of whiskey and sweat, and from the fear that squeezed the breath from her lungs. She edged forward, holding the valise in front of her face like a shield.

He continued to block her way, waving his arms and zigzagging from one side of the road to the other. Florence was sure the man had to be a maniac but she pressed on, making little progress. The sun dropped below the horizon while Florence continued to gain one yard at a time on the road, dodging the waving arms. At last, she saw the lane leading to the Pederson farm. With a new burst of energy, she raced past the man and headed for the light in the kitchen window. He did not follow but stood in the lane, calling after her in his hoarse voice, "Hey, girl!"

Running, stumbling, hoping the dogs would be locked in the barn, she reached the porch door and wrenched it open. "Oh, my God," she cried. "There was a terrible man chasing me!"

Safe now in the kitchen, Florence leaned against the door and tried to catch her breath. Emma rushed into the room. "You poor dear! What happened? You look white as a ghost!"

Florence collapsed on a chair. "I met the most terrible tramp on the road. He was drunk and he wouldn't let me pass. He kept waving his arms and shouting at me." Florence felt the tears well up, now that the danger was over.

"You poor thing. Let me get you a glass of water." Emma went to the hand pump and Mr. Pederson strode into the kitchen with a sneer on his face.

"A tramp you say? Was this so-called tramp about five-feet-nine. Graying brown hair. Dark blue jacket that's too big for him?" Pederson's voice was edged with sarcasm.

"Yes. But how did you know?"

Harold Pederson gave her a look of disgust. "That so-called tramp was Harvey Stover. He's a neighbor over to the west and harmless as a dickey-bird. Harvey drinks too much but he wouldn't hurt a fly." He paused to fold his arms. "We've had supper. We couldn't wait any longer for someone who is always late."

Emma handed her the glass of water and Florence took a few hasty sips. She rose to her feet, brushed past Mr. Pederson and walked into her room. She didn't want to hear any more of his lecture on how everything was always her fault. Still trembling, Florence undressed and got ready for bed. She was too angry and upset to feel hungry.

A few minutes later, a gentle tap, tap, tap sounded on her bedroom door. Emma came in, bearing a tray with a plate of cold sliced pork, some bread, a little jar of mustard and a cup of cocoa.

"I'm so sorry, Florence. Harold didn't realize how frightened you were. He didn't mean to act so ugly. Please forgive him."

Florence sighed. This was getting to be an all-too-familiar refrain.

Chapter Nine
Ida's Wedding and the Small Pox

Emma, did I tell you I got a letter from Emily Beckstrom? My dressmaker in Fargo. She bought yellow crepe for my bridesmaid's dress. Do you think that color is too spring-like for a January wedding?"

Florence brushed a bit of flour from her nose one chilly Saturday morning in November, while watching Emma knead the bread dough. The bridesmaid's dress would cost more than she had planned, so Florence had sacrificed her usual weekend at the Merchant's Hotel.

Emma placed the lump of dough into a big bowl to let it rise. "Yellow should brighten up a January day. The color will be lovely with your dark hair."

"What do you think about a V-neck trimmed with lace? Emily says that is the latest style." Florence had become used to these hurried conversations while Harold Pederson was out of the house. She and Emma had a tacit understanding not to discuss anything while he was around—anything that he would just ridicule, such as cooking lessons and chatter about a bridesmaid's dress.

"I think whatever you decide will be perfect. You will look just beautiful. Now let's have some coffee while we wait for the bread. When the dough puffs up high enough,

I'll punch it down and let it rise again." Emma sighed. "You know, Florence, I'd give anything to trade places with you. I'd love to be young again and feel excited about a wedding."

Florence didn't know how to respond to that. Emma almost never complained about her lot in life. Her landlady was like two different people—one lighthearted and gay when the two of them were alone together, the other nervous and tense whenever her husband was in the house. Now the light-hearted Emma poured the coffee and smiled, before she happened to glance out the kitchen window.

"Look, Florence! There's someone coming up the drive in a horse and buggy. I can't see who he is. Do you think you might be having a gentleman caller? Now he's getting out of the buggy. Oh my, he looks very handsome!"

"A caller? For me?" Florence never invited anyone to the Pederson house. She knew better than that. She did all her socializing elsewhere.

"Come and see, Florence. Do you know who he is?"

Florence hurried to the kitchen window and watched a young man tie the horse's reins to the porch rail. He was wearing an overcoat and a city hat. She couldn't believe it. Of all people. . .it was Leonard Kvam! So many months had passed since their last meeting, she thought he had forgotten all about her. She opened the kitchen door to greet him.

"Hello, Miss Thompson. . . Florence. Do you mind if I come in?"

The surprise of seeing him again almost took her breath away. "Oh yes. Come in. But how in the world did you know where I live?"

"I have ways of knowing these things," he said with a smile. "It wasn't too hard, actually. I called Miss Thorson and asked her. It's too bad you don't have a telephone here. I would have called first. But then I decided to take the chance you might be home."

"Don't just stand there on the porch," Emma called. "Come sit in the parlor where you two can have some privacy. I need to stay in the kitchen and keep an eye on the bread."

After Florence made the introductions, and after they were seated on the Pederson's stiff-backed settee, Leonard took Florence's hand in his. "This is going to sound a little strange, but I've come to say goodbye. I'll be leaving soon and I couldn't do that without seeing you again."

"Goodbye? Are you going away? But why?"

"I can't live at home any longer. I just can't do it and my father can't afford to keep me in school. You see . . . well, he just got married. To Mrs. Offerdahl, the housekeeper. She has a family and her four kids have moved in. Our house is so small. . .it's a bit crowded to say the least. I'm not accomplishing anything at home, anyway. So I've decided to go on the road."

Florence could hardly take it all in. His father re-married. And to a divorcee, of all things. She'd heard about Mrs. Offerdahl. And why did Leonard come to call, just to say goodbye? What did it mean to go *on the road*? Most men she knew were farmers or shopkeepers or in some kind of a profession. What in the world was all this about?

Before Leonard could explain himself, Harold Pederson stuck his head in the parlor door. "And who might this be?" he asked in a booming voice.

Emma fluttered into the room. "Florence has a gentleman caller, Harold. Let's let them have a few minutes of privacy."

"I guess I can sit in my own parlor if I want to." Pederson plopped himself on his favorite easy chair and stared at Leonard with suspicion.

In a genial way, Leonard rose to his feet and extended his hand. "I'm Leonard Kvam. From Six Mile Grove Township. I've known Miss Thompson for a while, and I've just come to say goodbye. I can't stay long."

Pederson raised his eyebrows. "This is my parlor. I guess you two can go outdoors, if you want to talk."

"Let's do that," Florence said. "I'll get my jacket."

A few minutes later, out in the farmyard, Florence lifted her head to gaze up at Leonard. She almost had forgotten how tall he was. "Is your landlord always this disagreeable?" he asked.

"Yes. Always. I'm kind of used to it now. But let's not talk about him. Please tell me more about what you are planning to do. I just don't understand."

Leonard turned up the collar of his coat against the chill breeze. "I know this is kind of sudden. But Florence, I had to see you before I left. I need to get out in the world and learn about business. So I'm going to start in a small way by selling novelties. My father is lending me his horse and buggy."

"Sell novelties?" This idea seemed incomprehensible. "How? Like a peddler going around to farmhouses? I just don't understand."

"I'm going to call on stores in various towns and try to sell them my line of goods. I won't have much of an inventory at first. I'll start with a few trinkets. Inexpensive things like fancy hair combs and brooches."

"But why can't you wait until spring? Why start now when winter is coming? I'd love for you to stay for my aunt Ida's wedding. I'm sure she would invite you, if I asked her."

"I can't stay home any longer, Florence. But I want you to know that I've thought about you so many times this past year. I want to get to know you better. I wonder if I could call on you the next time I'm around this part of the county."

"Of course you can. Any time at all. I'll look forward to it."

He took her hand again. "So will I."

Leonard smiled that funny wry smile, that wistful smile she remembered so well from the ride in his cutter. He had seemed so young and carefree then, as if he could do almost anything he wanted. But now. . .now he seemed burdened and terribly alone. He seemed to be grasping at any thin straw he could find, to get away from home.

He lifted her fingers to his lips. "Goodbye, Florence. Until next time."

Leonard climbed into the driver's seat and waved a last farewell. With a lump in her throat, she realized he must have wanted to see her very much, to go to all this trouble to find her. His life on the farm must be unbearable, she thought, to make him set off on such a madcap adventure. But it was reassuring to know that he cared for her. During this brief visit, he had made that much very clear.

The following weeks flew by and after presenting a Christmas program at school, Florence went to Grandmother's again for Christmas vacation. The family talked of nothing but wedding plans. Now it was all decided the ceremony would be at Jenny and Robert's house in Benson. But how many should be invited? Who would prepare the wedding dinner? How much food would be needed for the reception? And who could arrange the sleds to transport the wedding guests from Benson out to the farm?

Of vital importance was what the men should wear for a 10 a.m. ceremony. Ida had consulted Godey's Ladies Book—the Bible of fashion—which dictated striped trousers and morning jackets, but Rudolph and his brother Henry, the Best Man, would have none of that. Who should decide about the music? Bernice or Ida? Bernice was a self-taught musician, and she would have her own ideas about the proper selections.

All these matters were spinning in Florence's head while Grandmother continued to fret over the list of wedding guests, which seemed to grow longer and longer each day. There were nine brothers and sisters in the Johnson family, numerous Hansons and spouses, not to mention a host of friends. When Ida added it up, the number for the reception would be almost sixty.

"Sixty!" Grandmother looked worried. "Whatever will we do if a snow storm comes up? What if all these people can't get home? Remember, Ida, we have only one privy."

"The weather can't *dare* be bad," Ida declared. "There will be only sixteen at the ceremony. That's as many as we can fit into Jenny's house and her Ladies' Aid at church has agreed to help serve the wedding dinner. At least we don't need to worry about that anymore."

Florence could see that Ida hadn't quite reconciled herself to a winter wedding and the problems that entailed. Winter or summer, the roads were always a constant worry. Which was worse—snow or frozen mud?

As soon as the holiday was over, the members of the wedding party met at the photographer's studio, carrying their finery in big boxes. Josie Johnson, Rudolph's sister, had made Ida's wedding dress, since Ida didn't have time to make one herself. It was a beautiful white satin trimmed with lace. The 'something borrowed' was the wedding veil, which had been worn by Ida's youngest sister, Oline. She couldn't attend the wedding, now that she was living like a pioneer in a cabin in northern Minnesota, married to a woodcutter and stuck with a brood of children.

Henry and Rudolph had settled on dark business suits and had their shirts stiffly starched for the occasion. Once the four were assembled at the studio, Ida decided to discuss some new-fangled ideas about poses.

"I don't want us to look so old-fashioned, like Oline's wedding pictures," she said. "With the groom seated on a chair and the bride standing like a servant next to him. Why can't we try something new and different?

"I'd like *one* normal wedding picture," Rudolph grumbled, half in jest. "We've always used that same pose in my family."

"I gave in about the winter wedding," Ida said. "Now you can give in about the pictures. To me, the old way looks so stiff and formal. Let's have at least one picture with the groom standing and the bride sitting."

With the utmost patience, the photographer accommodated with all the poses the wedding party suggested—close-ups and full figure shots, seated and standing. The picture Florence liked best, the one given to her by Ida later, was the most unique of all. In this photograph, Ida sat on a big, lacy rattan chair with the photographer's crown of satin flowers on her head, veil flowing behind. She held a huge bouquet of silk roses since fresh ones were not available in the winter. Ida insisted on wearing her new rimless glasses and peeking out from under her skirt, one could see the white satin slippers Ida had found in a catalogue.

Florence sat perched on the arm of the chair, on Ida's left, with a clutch of silk flowers pinned at her waist, her serene gaze fastened on some distant spot. The other three in the wedding party stared straight into the camera, looking composed and grim. Henry in his suit and tie stood next to Florence and Rudolph, straight and tall, slightly behind Ida. It was a pose that was destined never to become popular in anyone's wedding album.

On New Year's Day evening, a-twitter with excitement, Bernice, Florence and Ida spent the night at the home of Jenny and Robert. They needed to be fresh and properly dressed for the morning ceremony. As soon as they awakened, all three rushed to the window to check on the weather. It looked brisk and cold and there was an adequate covering of snow on the ground. The sleds shouldn't have any trouble in transporting the guests.

Florence helped arrange the sixteen chairs in the parlor for the ceremony and the guests began to arrive. At the appointed time, along with Rudolph and Henry, the Rev. J.S. Strand took his place next to the square parlor table that served as an altar. He was dressed in the proper Lutheran vestments with a bright red embroidered stole for the Christmas season over a black robe. Bernice stuck a chord at the pump organ and played "*O Promise Me*" as an overture, and Florence escorted the smiling bride into the parlor. Neither Bernt nor Julius was available for this duty, since the brothers had to be at the farm getting ready for the reception.

The brief ceremony from the Lutheran prayer book took all of twenty minutes and Ida and Rudolph were pronounced man and wife. Afterward, everyone milled about in the crowded parlor, exclaiming about the beautiful and touching ceremony. Promptly at noon, the church ladies served the wedding dinner.

The occasion was so festive that at first, hardly anyone noticed the abrupt change in the weather. There had been a light breeze all morning but suddenly, the breeze picked up momentum and turned into a gusty gale. Snow swirled up against the windows and Ida, always the watchful one, didn't fail to notice.

"Just look at the way this wind is blowing! All the snow is gone from the street. The country roads must be blown bare, too. How are we going to get to the reception? Now we can't use the sleds," Ida wailed.

"Yes, we *can* use the sleds," Rudolph declared. "All we need to do is find some fields along the way, where there is plenty of snow. And not use the roads. Let's go before all the snow is completely gone."

Ida's Wedding, January 1915. Left to right: Rudolph, Ida, Florence, Henry Johnson

Rudolph and Henry took charge, herding their parents and kinfolk into their sleds, bundling them up against the cold. The Johnson sleds began the caravan, crunching over the windblown street, heading for the fields just beyond. After all the guests had departed, Henry hitched his team of horses to the last of the wooden sleds, and tried to hurry everyone along. He placed Rudolph in the back seat between Ida and Bernice.

"Cuddle up to Rudolph," he said. "The new groom can keep you warm."

"Don't fuss over me," Ida said. "I brought my own blanket. Let Rudolph and Bernice wrap up in the extra one you have."

Under skies the color of slate, Florence climbed in next to Henry in the front seat. Wearing a heavy winter coat, she pulled her knit cap down over her ears. Henry tucked a blanket around the two of them and headed for the nearest field. By now, it was hard to find any snow that had not been blown away, and Henry followed a zigzag route, hunting for patches of white.

"I wish I had brought a warmer coat," Bernice complained, edging closer to Rudolph. "How much longer will it take to get to Grandmother's?"

"Bernice, you look like the bride," Henry joked. "All snuggled up to Rudolph." He turned to give a wink to Ida, who sat self-contained as an Indian squaw, wrapped in a separate blanket. "Are you sure you're warm enough, Ida?

"I'm warm enough, Henry. You just hurry and get us out to the farm before we all freeze to death."

The wedding party sled crept across the fields, far behind the others. The cold wind whipped at Florence's face and the overcast sky refused to send down even a sprinkling of flakes. The scratchy sound of sled runners on bare ground filled Florence with despair. What a disastrous end to a perfect wedding. When would they ever get to Grandmother's? By now, she must be frantic with worry.

Two hours later, the wedding sled arrived in Betsy's front yard, and the men jumped out to unhitch the horses and take them to the barn. Florence pushed open the kitchen door, followed by Ida and Bernice, to find the reception in full swing. Uncle Bernt's hot toddies had put everyone into a jovial mood. After warming themselves near the woodstove, the women went upstairs to repair their wedding finery.

Once she felt presentable again, Florence found the dining room table loaded with wonderful food, sliced ham and blood sausage, lefse and cheese, rosettes and every kind of Norwegian pastry that Grandmother knew how to create. Berndt was playing the latest popular tunes on the fiddle with Bernice on the organ. Then Ida took a turn on the organ, pumping away in her satin slippers. Everyone was having a wonderful time and then, just when several guests started to talk about leaving, the gray twilight sky seemed to open up, sending down blankets and blankets of snow, making mounds of white over the open sleds parked in the yard, and covering the roads and the fields.

"Now what will we do?" cried Grandmother, her face wrinkled with worry. "Just look at all this snow!" Her worst fear was coming true. All these sixty people would have to stay overnight and she could just imagine the long lines outside at the privy.

Now Ida took charge. "You just go to bed, Mother. Let me worry about it. These folks can find a place to sleep and leave in the morning. We've all managed to make do in a snowstorm before."

Ida settled her new in-laws and the older guests in the bedrooms. She changed into one of her every-day dresses and spent her wedding night sleeping on the parlor floor next to Rudolph, amid a noisy crowd of wedding guests drinking the last of the hot toddies. Florence and Bernice changed into other dresses and stayed up most of the night, talking and joking with Henry and Bert Johnson and some of the other young men. Everyone thought this winter wedding was one they never would forget.

The next morning dawned clear and crisp. The guests finished off the last of the wedding food for breakfast and the men brushed snow off the sleds and retrieved the horses from the barn. In total exhaustion, the wedding guests left for home and Henry took the bridal couple to their new house in Benson. It never occurred to Rudolph to think about a honeymoon. Such an extravagance was only for rich people and not for shopkeepers. Rudolph had to be back at work on Monday.

Florence packed her valise and put her bridesmaid dress back into its box. She bade her last farewells to Bernice and the rest of the family and climbed into the family sled. Uncle Bernt was ready to take her back to the Pederson farm.

After all that excitement, Christmas and the wedding and the snowstorm, life with Emma and Harold seemed even more dreary and confining. Florence spent every weekend possible at the Merchant's Hotel. The weeks flew fly and then one wintry Friday evening, about mid-March, the girls gathered around the piano as usual. Petra Hamre tried to coax Florence to sing.

"I can't tonight," she said. "My throat is so sore, I couldn't get out a single note. Some other time."

She'd had a hard week at school. Some of the children were out sick with small pox or diphtheria, and it was difficult to juggle the lesson work so the absent ones wouldn't have too much trouble in catching up. She felt extra-tired that Friday from the long walk to Holloway. Her head was starting to ache.

Mrs. Severson liked to sit in the parlor with the young teachers, and now she looked at Florence with concern. "You don't look a bit well, dear. You should go to bed. Remember, my room is right next to yours. If you need anything during the night, just rap on the wall. I'll hear you."

Florence agreed. Feeling more sick and dizzy by the moment, she went upstairs to undress. She fell into a fitful sleep, only to wake a few hours later. Her throat felt so raw, she could hardly swallow. Her head throbbed with fever. Florence tried to sit up and rap on the wall, but the strength would not come. She felt riveted to the bed, unable to even lift her arm. She tossed and turned, longing for a drink of water and then about dawn, she heard someone come into the room. Florence saw Mrs. Severson bending over the bed.

"My God!" The proprietor's eyes flew open in horror. "Florence, let me get a closer look at your face. Turn to the light. My God, you've got small pox!"

"Small pox!" Florence was seized with fear. This was like hearing a sentence of death. Entire families in her district had been destroyed by small pox, a dread disease that was highly contagious. No one knew for certain what caused it, only that few people ever recovered.

"Are you sure?" she asked.

"Your face is broken out. I know the signs. I've seen it too often. I have to get you out of here before anyone knows. Small pox can spread like wildfire. This could ruin my business."

In her haze of fever and distress, Florence knew that Mrs. Severson was right. Just a rumor of small pox could close down the Merchant's Hotel and put everyone in quarantine. What could she do? Where could she go? The hospital wouldn't take victims of small pox. It was too contagious.

She heard Mrs. Severson leave, and then return in a few minutes with Petra Hamre in tow. "Florence, I'm so sorry to do this. It breaks my heart. But you have to get dressed now. Petra will get you out of here, before anyone sees you."

Florence felt herself being pulled from under the covers, woolen underwear rolled up her legs, her long dress thrown over her head, heavy coat buttoned up, an unfamiliar big hat with a long heavy veil clamped on her head. She was dimly aware of Petra at her side, holding her arm, being guided down the stairs and across the front parlor. She felt a cold blast of air hit her face as they stepped outdoors. Through the veil, Florence could see that Petra looked terribly frightened.

"Where can we go, Florence? What can we do?"

Florence's head cleared a little. "Let's go to the depot. We can go to my aunt Ida's house in Benson. That's the only place I can think of. I'm sure Ida will take me in."

Florence waited on a bench in the depot, huddled in her coat, while Petra bought the tickets. The dinky pulled in and they boarded, Petra half-dragging Florence up the steps and to the rear seat of the passenger car.

"What's that noise I hear?" she asked. "What's going on?"

"It's some kind of school outing," Petra replied. "The car is filled with children. Keep your veil down and don't look around. Don't let anyone notice you."

Florence leaned against the coldness of the window-pane, fearful she might infect Petra, fearful she might infect all the children on the dinky. Her head throbbed during the half-hour ride and then she was out in the cold again, the wind whipping at her veil and as she tried to keep it down over her face.

"Which way?" cried Petra. "Where does Ida live?"

Florence started down the main street and turned a corner she thought looked familiar. She had been to the house a few times before the wedding, while Ida had been moving in furniture and now, confused by the fever, she wasn't sure she could find it again.

"How much farther, Florence?" Petra gasped as the wind swirled snow in their faces.

They reached the corner and Florence recognized the two-story frame house, the stable in back, the front porch. "Here. Here it is. Knock on the door and pray that Ida is home."

In a few minutes, the door opened slightly. Ida peered out at this apparition on her doorstep, the huge hat with the concealing veil. "Who is the world is this? What do you want?"

Florence lifted the veil. "It's me. Florence. I've got small pox."

"Oh, my God!" Ida slammed the door shut.

Florence felt her head spin and she clutched Petra for support. She couldn't think of anything to do, other than die right here on Ida's doorstep. Then the front door opened a little and Ida peeked out. "Are you sure?"

"I'm afraid so. Please let me in, Ida. Let me stay. I have nowhere to go. I'll try not to be any trouble."

The door opened a little wider. "All right, then. Come in." She nodded at Petra and the two of them guided Florence up the stairs and into the spare bedroom. They undressed her and put her under the covers.

"You'd better go now," Ida said to Petra. "Thanks for bringing her here. I'll call the doctor."

Florence heard the retreating footsteps and realized that capable Ida had taken charge; that her life might be saved after all. She fell into a grateful sleep.

A little later, Florence awoke to see a pompous little man with dark-rimmed spectacles pacing the room.

"Do you realize that you have small pox, young lady? And I'm told that you took the train here and exposed a carload of school children! I could have an epidemic on my hands. And you—a schoolteacher! You should know better. You're supposed to be an intelligent person."

Florence shrank under the covers. "I had nowhere to go. I didn't know what to do."

"You will suffer for this outrage. You are a good-looking girl but you won't be good looking any longer. You will have deep, ugly pockmarks all over your face before this

fever is done with you. Serves you right. A teacher—
spreading an epidemic!"

The doctor stepped out in the hall and Florence could
hear the brief conference with Ida in hurried undertones.
The house would have to be fumigated at once and placed
in strict quarantine. Ida would have to send notice to Mr.
Pederson, to alert the parents at Florence's school. It
would have to be closed for at least two weeks.

Florence sank into a haze of fever as trays of food came
and went, the chamber pot was produced and carried off.
As her strength began slowly to return, Ida brought books
and newspapers, and tried to cheer her with messages of
hope from her fellow teachers and from faithful Emma.
Another week passed and the quarantine was lifted.

Florence worked up the courage to look in the mirror,
to see if the doctor's prediction had come true. Her complexion was clear and there wasn't a single pockmark left
on her body. She decided she could manage to go downstairs unaided.

"I don't know how to thank you," Florence said,
when she found Ida and Rudolph in the kitchen. They
looked exhausted from all the care-taking. "You saved my
life. There isn't any way I can ever make that up to you. If
you can let me stay just a couple more days, I should be
strong enough to go back to the Pederson's."

Florence felt close to tears. These good people had
placed themselves in such a fearsome predicament on her
behalf, had tended and cared for her, literally nursed her
back to life. But it wasn't the Norwegian way to show
much emotion about it all, or to become maudlin in her
expression of gratitude. They all knew small pox could be
a killer. Nothing more needed to be said about that.

Florence returned to school and within two weeks, she learned the tribulations had not ended for Ida and Rudolph. The predicted epidemic didn't occur but her two benefactors came down with small pox. Again, the house was placed in quarantine. The two recovered and neither one was left with disfiguring pockmarks. With the help of neighbors and friends, they also experienced a fortunate recovery.

Spring came late to Swift County that year. In spite of the chill in the air, Florence held a May Day program out-doors, complete with a ribbon bedecked May pole and a box social. Then she prepared for the next big festival — *syttende mai* — the Seventeenth of May. This was Norwegian Independence Day, a day celebrated in that part of Minnesota with more enthusiasm than the Fourth of July. This was a chance to offer her class a special history lesson on how this glorious day came about.

Florence had to do some homework herself, to untangle the many complexities of Norwegian history dating back to the days of the Vikings. Most of her pupils knew about celebrations in their own homes with special food and decorations, but they didn't know the background of it all. Florence presented a brief lecture on the long domination of Denmark and then of Sweden, before Norway declared its independence on the seventeenth of May, 1814, and adopted the Norwegian Constitution. But a new Norwegian king—Haakon VII— was not crowned until 1905. The time lapse always seemed a puzzle, especially to immigrants who had come to America long before then.

"Does anyone know why it took so long for Norway to crown its own king?" Florence asked her class.

One of the older girls raised her hand. "Because the Swedes were too stubborn to let Norway go."

"That's right," Florence said. "For a long time, Norway had a constitution and a parliament. But still had a Swedish king, one they didn't like at all. His name was Oskar and he thought Norway was too weak to be a country on its own. At last he gave in on this score, and time has proved that Oskar was wrong."

With this one exception concerning European history, Florence thought it was more important for the children to learn about the history of their own country. That was confusing enough with a war looming in Mexico and possibly in Europe.

Another school year came to an end and once again, Florence's desk was piled high with gifts from the children. It was difficult to say goodbye to her pupils, but even more difficult to say goodbye to Emma Pederson. On her last day, Florence found Emma in the kitchen, choking back tears.

"I hate to see you go, Florence. You've brought so many happy times to this house. I'll always remember our cooking lessons and all the fun we had, just talking together."

Florence hugged her landlady in a last farewell. Emma was the one who had made life bearable in the Pederson household, not the other way around. Without realizing it, Emma had taught some valuable lessons about endurance and compassion.

"Please don't cry, Emma. That makes me feel so bad."

"It's been a bad day all around. You are leaving and . . . and this morning while you were at school, our dog Satan died. You know he had been so sick . . ." Tears rolled down Emma's face.

Florence withdrew her consoling embrace. Both the dogs had been monsters ever since her arrival at the farm, always barking and snarling. The dogs never had gotten used to her, the way Harold Pederson had said they would.

"Well, Emma, try to look at it this way. With one dog gone, the next teacher who comes to board will need to be only *half* as afraid as I was. I'll never forget the day those dogs trapped me in the summer kitchen."

Emma burst into tears again and Florence heard the sound of carriage wheels approaching. Rudolph was coming to get her! She would spend the night with Ida and then she would board the Great Northern for Moorhead and another summer session at the Normal. This time, she would get her First Class Certificate for sure. Even more exciting, Florence had signed a contract to teach at District 88 in the fall, the same school where Ida had taught. That meant a raise to sixty-five dollars a month and a nice comfortable boarding place at the H.R. Hanson farm.

Everything in her life seemed to be looking up, except for the continuing silence from Leonard Kvam. She hadn't heard a word about his adventures on the road. In this case, she felt that no news was bad news. She had the feeling that Leonard's new career was not going so well at all.

May Day school program, Florence on far right. At Monson Lake about 1916.

Chapter Ten

The Six Mile Grove School District 88

J ust wait until you meet Dora," Rudolph chuckled. He gave Florence a teasing smile as they bounced along in his buggy, heading for the H.R. Hanson farm. After leaving summer school, Florence had spent a few days with the Johnsons to give Ida a hand with her fall housecleaning. That seemed a terribly small repayment for all their valiant help during the small pox episode.

"I don't recall anyone named Dora when Ida lived at the Hanson place," Florence said. She had visited there several times during Ida's tenure at District 88. She had met H.R., also known as Hans Rasmus, and his wife Britha. They had emigrated from Norway as a young couple, and now were about sixty. But no one else had been in the house.

"Dora is the unmarried daughter," Rudolph explained. "She was away last year, helping one of her brothers and his family. That's how it goes with spinsters, you know. Always at someone's beck and call for free maid and housekeeping services. Dora is back home now, running the place for her folks."

It was a warm Sunday afternoon, the day before Labor Day, and Florence felt glad she had worn a lightweight cotton dress. It was one of her favorites, sprigged with bright red rosebuds with a scoop neckline instead of a bodice buttoned up to her chin. The flowing sleeves just barely covered her elbows, and she wore a broad-brimmed hat in a matching red color.

The carriage rattled over a narrow wooden bridge that spanned a meandering creek, and Florence felt a tingle of delight. There, up ahead, was the imposing, two-story house, painted a glistening white and shaded by tall oaks, with a lush green lawn and lilac bushes that fronted the veranda. There wasn't a chicken or a pig to be seen in the Hanson front yard, which was fenced off from all the livestock. This was the richest farm in the county, a testimony to the hard work of successful immigrants.

"I see the three of them are waiting on the front porch to greet you," Rudolph said. "Dora is the tall lady. I just want to warn you. Dora is just as straight-laced as old H.R. himself."

Florence saw the three slender figures dressed in black. They looked as if they were going to a funeral. "Did someone die?" Florence asked.

Rudolph laughed. "The Hansons always wear black on Sundays. H.R. has some very strong ideas about sin. You wouldn't ever catch him wearing a bright color on a Sunday or any day. Just remember that to him, sin includes dancing and card-playing and riding in a buggy with a young man. When I was courting Ida, we hardly ever got a minute alone."

The situation concerning sin in Swift County was very hard to comprehend. Some Lutherans were extremely pious and other Lutherans, even if they were in the same family, had more relaxed ideas. The degree of strictness in the various synods often split a family in several directions. For example, Rudolph's mother, Kari, was a sister to H. R. Hanson, and yet her family loved to sing and dance and play whist every chance they could. These conflicting ideas caused all sorts of havoc and a teacher was expected to conform to whatever prevailed in her boarding place.

"I hope Mr. Hanson won't try to force any of his notions on me," Florence said. "I have my own ideas about what is sin and what is not." Florence noticed another figure dressed in black, a husky looking man with a ruddy face, coming around the side of the house. "Who is that?" she asked.

"That's Adolph. The new hired man. He's an immigrant from Germany and Adolph takes great pains to fit in the best way he can. Now don't let all this trouble you too much. Ida liked it here, in spite of the strait-laced ways. Just try not to ruffle any of H.R.'s feathers. Or any of Dora's either."

Rudolph pulled on the reins and the carriage stopped in front of the veranda. He helped Florence alight and made the introductions. With the help of Adolph, he carried Florence's trunk into the house.

"I'm very pleased to be here," Florence said with a gracious smile. She always had felt a little awestruck in the presence of H.R. Hanson, an outstanding pillar of the community. He had such an aristocratic bearing, with his chiseled features, deep-set eyes and drooping moustache. He had raised seven fine children, had served as a county commissioner for many years and was a founder of the Six Mile Grove Lutheran Church.

"It's the Sabbath, Miss Thompson." H.R. looked at her in a disapproving way, at the bright red hat and her frothy summer frock. "We will have supper at five o'clock. And afterward, there will be prayers and a Bible reading in the sitting room."

"You are welcome here, Miss Thompson," Dora said with a stiff smile. She wore a high-necked, black taffeta dress with long tight sleeves that came down to the wrist, with a narrow waist and a wide skirt that brushed the floor. Still, on this warm day, Dora managed to look cool and elegant, as if a drop of perspiration wouldn't dare to moisten her brow.

"Yes, you are very welcome," added Britha, who looked equally elegant in her black bombazine. Her expression was complacent and kind, as if she had learned long ago to accept whatever fate might have in store. Her hair was a startling white, twisted up in a topknot without a hair out of place.

Florence followed Dora into the vestibule, past the huge credenza with its oval mirror polished to a gleam, past the hall tree with its hooks and umbrella stand. The plank wood floor looked freshly waxed, each piece of Victorian furniture carefully arranged. With Dora in the lead, Florence ascended the broad staircase and walked down the long hall, to the room reserved for the boarding teacher. This was the room where Ida had slept, in the walnut bedstead covered with an exquisite wedding-ring quilt made by Britha. There was a massive bureau with claw-like feet, a square oak table and an overstuffed chair for reading.

"I'm sure you will be very comfortable here," Dora said primly. "Be prompt for supper. Father doesn't like it when anyone is late for the table blessing."

"Do I really have to attend prayers tonight, Dora? I'm a little tired and I'd like to rest."

"Everyone in the household attends prayers on Sunday evenings. Including Adolph." Dora closed the door with a quiet click.

Florence opened her trunk and began to unpack. Ida had warned the Sunday night sessions would be held in high Norwegian, and that H.R. tended to read more pages from the Bible than were absolutely necessary. Since Ida was bi-lingual, she had no problem with the high Norwegian. But Florence's little attempt to beg off hadn't been well received, so she resigned herself to a boring evening.

As she unpacked, her thoughts drifted back to her childhood in Canada, where her family had been expected to observe the "blue laws" of Estevan, Saskatchewan. Children were not allowed to play on the Sabbath, and that had been a hard cross to bear for a ten-year-old. Florence remembered sitting on the back step of her house, holding her doll, waiting for the sun to go down, wondering why the Good Lord wanted to make a little girl feel so miserable. It seemed a mystery then, and even more a mystery now in this supposedly more enlightened era.

At the supper table that evening, Adolph sat next to Florence. His dark hair was slicked back with pomade and the corners of his blue eyes were riddled with white squint-lines from working out in the fields. He couldn't have been more than thirty, and already seemed set in his ways as a confirmed bachelor. Adolph dutifully bowed his head when H.R. invoked God's blessing in Norwegian on the cold sliced ham and the pickle relish and the cold cabbage salad in his monotonous, sing-song voice. Obviously, the hired man had accepted the fact that nothing was cooked in the Hanson kitchen on a Sunday. All the meals were prepared a day ahead.

"How long have you been teaching, Miss Thompson?" asked Britha, as she carefully unfolded her linen napkin from its tortoise-colored ring.

"About a year and a half. I started mid-year in Swenoda Township, and then took the spring term at District One. Spring Creek. Last year I was at Holloway. I was very happy to get District 88 this year, now that Ida is married."

Britha asked more polite questions. Dora asked polite questions. H.R. looked with disdain at Florence's summer dress. She didn't own a black dress and promised herself never to buy one. Afterward, Florence helped Dora carry the dishes into the kitchen. "Can I help you to wash up?" she asked.

"It's the Sabbath, Miss Thompson. Dishwashing has to wait until tomorrow. Now it's time for prayers."

Dora led the way to the sitting room where the family had gathered. H.R. was seated in his easy chair next to an ornate kerosene lamp, which bathed the room in a rosy glow. Britha was on the Victorian settee and Adolph on a straight-back chair. Dora settled herself next to her mother, leaving Florence the only choice left, an armless, high-backed mahogany chair that forced one to sit tall as a ramrod. Dutifully and with as much grace as she could muster, Florence turned her attention to the Bible H. R. was holding, a huge, leather-bound book with gilt-edged pages. His pince-nez glasses hung from a looped black band around his neck and now he adjusted them on his nose. He scanned through the finely-wrought Norwegian script and placing his index finger on the proper verse, H.R. glanced around to be sure he had everyone's attention. Then he began to read aloud in his guttural, monotonous, sing-song voice.

Florence wiggled her toes inside her high-button boots and glanced at Adolph, who appeared to be studying the delicate yellow flower painted on the porcelain base of the lamp. The voice droned on as H.R. read verse after verse after verse. It seemed to take excruciatingly long for H.R. to arrive at the bottom of the page. The sound of the slow, steady voice made her eyelids grow heavy and she squirmed in the chair. A dull ache started at the base of her spine as she anticipated the pause that would signal the end of the passage. Minutes ticked by. More minutes ticked by. And then at last came the pause. A welcome beat of silence. Florence stood up, trying to stifle a sigh of relief. H.R. shot a stern look in her direction. With a loud harrumph, he cleared his throat and adjusted his glasses. Then slowly, carefully, he moistened his index finger and turned to the next page. Florence sank back into the hard, unforgiving chair.

The next day was Labor Day. Dora served a hearty breakfast of sausage, cheese, toasted bread and boiled eggs, and strong Scandinavian coffee. Afterward, Florence wandered out to the barn to look for Adolph, to ask for a tour.

He showed her the rows of immaculate cow stalls, the summer kitchen, the hog pen, the chicken coop and the tool shed with all the farm implements hung neatly on the walls. "Ya, this is a good place," Adolph said.

"This is the most beautiful farm I've ever seen," Florence agreed. Except for the Sunday evening prayers, she counted herself very lucky.

Early the following morning, Florence walked the quarter-mile through the apple orchard to the schoolhouse. She unlocked the door and made the usual preparations. The moment she went outdoors to ring the school bell, the thirty-five children trooped in, eager to meet the new teacher. The first day went well. Ida had done a good job with these pupils and Florence felt this would be her easiest school ever. It was a joy to follow a teacher who always had stressed good deportment.

District 88 Six Mile Grove School. Hans R. Hanson barn in background.

At her boarding place, Florence settled into the routine and stayed out of Dora's way. She was a whirlwind of cooking, washing and cleaning six days a week. She had no time for idle chatter, nor did Britha who busied herself with making quilts or working on Ladies Aid projects for the church. Florence yearned for some adult companionship and whenever she could, she escaped to Ida's house in Benson for the weekend.

One of their favorite topics was the upcoming county election, and whether or not the male citizens of Swift County would vote Lillie Thorson back into office. "It doesn't seem right that we, the teachers, have nothing to say about it," Florence said.

"I think Rudolph is going to vote for Tillie Thomason," Ida replied. "She's so much younger, only 28, and Tillie has more progressive ideas. He thinks it's time for a change."

As it turned out, Tillie won a hard-fought race and almost right away, she began to write a weekly column for the *Benson Review*. It was titled *Rural School Notes* and Florence devoured every word, feeling proud to be a part of all these changes in the school system. Tillie introduced the new Palmer Method of penmanship at the Teachers Institute that fall, a seminar designed for all the county teachers to attend.

After that, Florence held daily drills in her classes. She saw to it that each pupil above the Second Grade could draw satisfactory ovals on blue-lined theme paper. From there, the students progressed to cursive writing and learned to make proper tails on their "p"s and "q"s, and nice long loops on a "y" and "g". Florence felt certain that the Palmer Method would put an end forever to scrawly, unreadable handwriting.

Everything was going well at the Hanson household until one Saturday evening, when Bert Johnson invited Florence to go roller-skating at the new rink in Benson. She and Bert had become good friends, now that he worked at the hardware store and was a paying guest at Rudolph and Ida's. She saw him there often.

The roller rink was a delightful place, created in an abandoned schoolhouse by an enterprising businessman, and had become very popular with the young people as a place to meet and have a good time. It had a polished hardwood floor and a player piano to provide the music. Since Bert was a nephew to H.R. Hanson and such a respectable young man, Florence felt quite comfortable about accepting the date.

On that fateful evening, Bert arrived at the Hanson farm and chatted in the parlor with his uncle, while Florence was in the kitchen to give her face a quick wash with rainwater. She could hear the two talking in the other room and then, suddenly, there was silence. The next thing she knew, H.R. was in the kitchen looking thunderstruck.

"What is this I hear? That you and Bert plan to go roller-skating!"

"Yes. We do." Florence finished patting her face dry. "Do you think something is wrong with that?"

"Roller-skating is sinful, Miss Thompson. It is just as sinful as dancing. No self-respecting schoolteacher would do such a thing. You are expected to set a good example for the young people."

"Now what could be so wrong about roller-skating?" A tiny knot of rebellion was beginning to form in the pit of her stomach.

"You would have a man's arm around you. That is what's wrong. I was young once, Miss Thompson. I know all about what can lead to sinful thoughts."

"Now Mr. Hanson. Please. When you roller-skate with a young man, you don't get so close to him as all that. All the young couples just hold hands and skate around in a big circle to the music. That's all."

Florence could feel the knot tighten. She never had tried to cross H.R. Hanson in any way. She had gone along with the Bible-reading whenever she couldn't find any way to escape; she had attended church with the family; she never had bothered Dora in any way. True, she hadn't bought a black dress to wear on Sundays. She had drawn a line about that. But after all, she was a paying guest in this house. She had a right to some kind of a social life.

H.R. folded his arms with a note of finality. "Roller-skating is sinful."

"Roller-skating is fun. All the young people do it. And it's good exercise, too. I don't see anything wrong with it. And I'm going."

Florence brushed past H.R. and went into the parlor to meet Bert. "Let's go. I'm all ready." She grabbed him by the arm and they walked out the front door without looking back.

A few minutes later, seated in Bert's carriage, Florence couldn't help but laugh. "You must think I'm a complete hellion, to stand up to your uncle like that."

The Six Mile Grove School, District 88   203

"I didn't think old H.R. would get so upset about a little roller-skating," Bert said. "Dancing, yes. He would raise a ruckus about that. I just hope I didn't make trouble for you."

"Your uncle has his ideas and I have mine. I've wanted to go skating ever since the rink opened. And I'm glad you asked me. I like to dance too, and I don't see anything wrong with that, either. After all, these are modern times. We don't live in the Dark Ages anymore."

Bert laughed. "Maybe *you* don't live in the Dark Ages. But here in Six Mile Grove, most people still do. That's one reason why I moved to Benson to room with Rudolph and Ida. Let's not worry about old H.R. He'll get over it."

They left for the roller-rink but Florence wasn't so sure about H.R., or how quickly he would forget about the scene in his kitchen. He was a man who was used to running things *his* way.

Every country teacher was expected to make at least one social call on each family in her district, every year. This was a time-consuming duty and a difficult one to fulfill, if the teacher didn't have any means of transportation. But the Hansons were generous about letting her borrow their horse and buggy, and so Florence set about completing this task.

She saw some strange goings-on in her district but uppermost in her mind, was the need to guard her tongue and respect the privacy of each family. She never wanted to find herself accused of spreading gossip. That was a fatal trap for any teacher.

This situation was particularly burdensome because of Rose Ecklund. Rose was a neighbor of Ida's and a former teacher, who thrived on gossip. She often dropped into Ida's house without any notice, just to chew the fat. Ida didn't mind too much, since Rose was an expert fiddle player and often joined Rudolph in a duet. Sometimes Ida would accompany them on the piano. These evening musicales could be fun, except when Rose started pumping Florence with nosy questions.

"Is it true the Horshams in your district, don't have a privy?"

"Is Oscar Olafson as tight as people say?"

"Did the Torgersons sell some acreage for seed money?"

"Why won't you tell me what you had to eat, the night you went to the Bruchet's for dinner? I hear the French eat strange things. Like snails."

The questions went on and on, especially about the Bruchets. The French family that had settled in her district, were like a piece of flotsam carelessly tossed into an ocean of Norwegian tidyness. Even Florence, who had become accustomed to the oddities of certain farm families, had felt aghast after her visit to the Bruchet household. She had seen tiny, new-born piglets rooting around in the kitchen, the playmates of the Bruchet toddlers. But she never in the world would have mentioned such a thing to Rose Ecklund. The news would be all over the county.

"Is it true the Bruchets pick mushrooms in their pasture? How can they tell which are the poisonous ones? You know the French love to eat mushrooms."

Rose looked at Florence in a piercing way, after one of their musical evenings at the Johnson house. Rose worked at the Benson Dry Goods Store on Main Street and loved to gossip with all the customers. Everyone knew that Rose liked to listen in on other people's conversations on the party line. She made no secret of that.

"I don't know anything about mushrooms or snails," Florence said. "I don't know where you hear such things."

"Don't think for a minute you are fooling me, Florence," Rose pouted. "I was a teacher once myself. I know all about calling on these farm families, and the strange things you see. I could write a book."

"Well, you write one, then. But my lips are sealed."

Ida's snoopy neighbor was far from Florence's mind one wintry Saturday morning. There had been a heavy snow-fall the night before and Ida had invited her to come for the weekend. But how could she get to Benson with the snow still falling? H.R. would never let her ask Adolph for a ride on a day like this. Then she hit on the idea of calling some of the neighbors. Down in the kitchen, she found Dora busily sifting flour for her Saturday baking.

"Is it all right to make a few telephone calls? I want to see if anyone around here might be going to town."

"On a day like this? You certainly get some far-fetched ideas. But go ahead, if you want to. The listings are in a book in that drawer."

Florence rang up neighbor after neighbor with no suc-cess, while Dora kept on with her baking with a smug, "I-told-you-so" smile on her face. Then as a last resort, Florence thought of Mr. Bruchet. She rang him up with her request, while Dora pretended not to listen.

"Mon Dieu! A ride to town! Have you looked out-doors?"

"Yes, I know, Mr. Bruchet. It's still snowing. But I have to get to Benson. My aunt invited me and I hate to disappoint her."

"Well, Miss Thompson, I'm going to leave in a little while. But I don't think you would want to ride with me. I'm taking a sled full of hogs."

"I don't mind that. I wouldn't have to sit in the back with the pigs, would I?"

Dora almost dropped her sifter. "You are the very limit, Miss Thompson. The idea—of riding to town with the Bruchet's pigs! Any sensible person would stay home on a day like this."

"Oh, thank you, Mr. Bruchet," Florence shouted into the telephone. "I'll meet you down at the road in half an hour."

She gave Dora a triumphant look and raced upstairs to pack her valise. She wouldn't need to sit through any long boring Sunday night prayers this weekend. She could stay at Ida's just as late as possible. Clad in long woolen tights under her skirt, her heavy winter coat, boots, with her head wrapped in a thick woolen scarf, Florence waited on the road for the French farmer and his pigs. He came along in a few more minutes, driving a team of big sturdy plow horses that pulled a wooden sled-full of huge squealing hogs. Florence couldn't have felt more delighted.

"Hello, Mr. Bruchet! This is so kind of you. I'll find my own way to get back home."

"I'm sure you will," he replied, and helped her up to the driver's seat beside him. "You seem to be good at finding a way to do things." He urged the horses forward and they started off down the road.

Main Street looked deserted when Florence jumped off the sled a little later. She thanked her kind neighbor again as the wind blew a swirl of snow in her face. Then she trudged the few blocks to the Johnson house and knocked on the door.

"Land sakes," said Ida, ushering Florence inside. "I didn't think you'd make it on a day like this. Take off those boots, and I'll find you some slippers. And let me hang up your coat. It's soaking wet."

"I almost didn't make it," Florence replied, and told Ida the story about her ride with the pigs. "Now don't you dare breathe a word of this to Rose Ecklund. She's always quizzing me about the Bruchet family. I call her Rosy the Nosy. Let's just keep her guessing."

"Rose isn't so bad. Just born with too much curiosity. Now don't worry. I won't say a word about it."

The two spent the afternoon baking cookies and just when Ida put on the coffee pot, Rose Ecklund strolled in the kitchen door. Rose never bothered to knock first, and always made herself right to home.

"Why, Florence! What a surprise to see you here. I was just on my way home from work, and I didn't see a horse or a sled come into town all day. How did you ever get here, in all this snow?"

"I'm not going to tell you, so just stop asking." Florence liked to tease Rose, although she knew the inquisitive one would never stop asking.

"Oh, come on. Tell," Rose said. "I know you weren't here last night because I was here myself." She helped herself to a cookie and poured a cup of coffee. "It's a mystery to me, how you get around the way you do, living so far out in the country."

Florence glanced at Ida and suppressed a giggle. She glanced out the window, pretending to be fascinated by the drifts of snow, and began to hum a favorite song: *If I Had the Wings of an Angel.*

Ida went to the piano and picked up the tune. Florence began to sing the words,

"Over these prison walls I would fly" and Ida added an "oink, oink" at the end of the phrase. The two sang the entire song this way, with plenty of oink, oinks. Rose was not amused.

"Just don't think for a minute that you can make me the butt of your private joke. This isn't funny at all. There's something fishy here. Now tell. How did you get to town in all this snow?"

"That's for me to know and you to find out," Florence said. "Have another cookie and forget about the way I travel."

"Oink, oink," agreed Ida.

The following weekend turned out to be a sunny one, and Florence had no trouble getting a ride to town with Adolph. Once again, Rose strolled into Ida's kitchen on Saturday afternoon and this time, there was a self-satisfied smile on her face.

"I know how you got to town last weekend, Florence Thompson. I knew you couldn't fool me for long."

"You know?" Florence glanced at Ida in surprise. She was sure Ida hadn't spilled the beans but there was no stopping Rose, once she had her mind made up.

"Carrie Thorstrup told me. One of my customers at the store. I'd been asking everyone all week about you. And how in the world you got to town last Saturday. Then Carrie told me she *saw* you jump off Mr. Bruchet's sled.

And the sled was full of pigs! Now I understand about all those 'oink, oinks'! I said you couldn't fool me for long."

This time, it was Rose's turn to have the last laugh. But Florence didn't mind too much. Her reputation had stayed untarnished. No one could accuse her of being a gossip, and that was what really mattered.

Chapter Eleven

Glimmers of Love

"What this place needs is a little elbow grease," sniffed Dora after Christmas vacation. She wiped a finger across the treasured marble-top table in the front parlor. "This house doesn't look the same since we moved to Benson."

"Julia hasn't been feeling well," Florence said. "She has been in bed ever since I returned. Perhaps the excitement of moving was too much for her."

The sudden decision of Mr. and Mrs. Hanson to retire and move to town had been a big surprise to Florence. Upon her return from Christmas vacation, she discovered that Henry, one of the Hanson sons, and his wife Julia had taken charge of the farm. Something close to a revolution had taken place. There was no more Bible reading in the parlor on Sunday evenings; it was all right to cook food on the Sabbath. Dora's immaculate housekeeping standards were all but forgotten.

"Say what you like, Florence," Dora said on this visit to her former home. "But I know that Julia is just bone-lazy. That's *all* that's the matter with her."

In truth, the doctor could find nothing wrong with Julia. She complained about her head, her back, her feet, and had found every excuse to stay in bed. If it hadn't been for her mother Hazel, who had moved in to help care for baby Blanche, the operation of the household would have come to a standstill.

"How do you like living in Benson," Florence asked, wanting to ease away from the subject of Julia and all her maladies.

"It's more convenient, I must admit. But the house we rented is so small I hardly have a thing to do. I truly miss the farm."

Florence couldn't imagine anyone missing the isolation of a farm, or not enjoying life in town. Country living was beginning to wear her down.

More changes came that January, other than the retirement of H. R. Orin Kvam, Leonard's fifteen-year-old brother, had come back to school in an effort to complete the Eighth Grade. Orin was an indifferent student, full of mischief. One day he let it slip that Leonard was home again, that his brother's venture on the road had turned out to be a complete failure. Orin looked so much like Leonard it made her heart ache, especially when Orin told her about the troubles with the new stepmother, Mrs. Offerdahl. Orin still called her by such a formal name.

"Why can't you try to get along with her?" Florence asked.

"She's so bossy, always finding work for us to do. She thinks the house is all hers now. She gets so upset when she catches Leonard reading. It's too cold up in our bedroom, so he reads in the kitchen with his feet propped up on the fender of the coal stove. That gives Mrs. Offerdahl a fit. She says Leonard is lazy. I know he doesn't like to milk the cows. I get stuck with that, most of the time. Her kids are too young to help much with the chores."

After her talk with Orin, Florence realized that Leonard had been home for months without making any effort to see her. At first she felt deeply hurt. Then she thought he must feel too ashamed about his failure on the road, and the way he had come home with his tail between his legs. She decided to cheer him up and invite him to a tag dance coming up on Saturday night. That was the kind of dance where the girls ask the men to be their escorts, so asking him wouldn't appear too forward. She summoned her courage and dialed his party-line number, hoping not too many people would pick up the receiver to listen in.

"Is this really you, Florence? What a surprise," Leonard said. "It's so good to hear from you. Did you say this would be a tag dance? Well, I'd like to go Saturday night, but I'm afraid I don't know how to dance."

"I can teach you. You're missing out on a lot of fun, by not going to the dances."

"There's another problem. My cousin Johanna invited me but I said 'no' . . . mostly because I'm not much of a dancer. If I go with you, she'd feel very hurt," Leonard replied.

"Invite her to come along. The three of us can go together."

"Are you sure that would be all right?"

"I'm sure Johanna wouldn't mind at all. You call her and say the three of us will go. Can you pick me up on Saturday, then? About seven o'clock?"

"I'll pick you up in the cutter, Florence. Remember the great ride we had after that Valentine program?" He hesitated. "Thank you for calling. You've made me feel much better about coming home again. That was something I really didn't want to do, believe me."

Florence hung up, thinking sometimes men could be so dense about these things. Johanna had probably asked him only because she didn't want to go to the dance unescorted. They were cousins, after all. She felt pleased there would be no need to have a confrontation with Henry and Julia. They wouldn't care one whit if she went to a dance. She lived in a different world, now that the younger generation had taken charge of the farm. Times were certainly changing.

On the following Saturday evening, only a few heads turned to stare when the three young people walked into the Town Hall. It might have ignited some speculation if Florence and Leonard had gone to the dance as a couple. Then tongues would have wagged for certain. But as it was, Johanna was a popular girl and didn't lack for dancing partners, while Florence had Leonard all to herself, trying to teach him some new steps. He just couldn't seem to feel the steady rhythm of the fiddle music.

"I guess I can learn, eventually," he said after they had bumped into the same couple for the third time. "I doubt I'll ever be as good as you are, though. Let's sit this one out."

They found some chairs in a corner of the room and watched the other couples swing around the dance floor. Leonard loosened his collar. "I hope you don't think I'm too big a dud."

"I don't think that at all. I've had more opportunities

to dance than you have. I used to go to dances all the time at the Normal."

"Before now, I never thought it was very important to learn. You know, Florence, I rather envy you. You seem so settled in what you want to do with your life. And I'm just floundering around."

"You must have learned something out on the road. It couldn't have been a total loss."

"I learned a lot about salesmanship. What to say and what not to say. And I learned a hard lesson about money and how quickly it can go. You need a lot of that green stuff to get started in business." He smiled in his wry, wistful way.

"So many young people are leaving the farm these days, and going to a city. How about trying your luck in Minneapolis?"

"It's the same old problem. No money to get started."

"Listen, I hear a waltz. Are you ready to try again? This one sounds slow and easy." She drifted into his arms, thinking he was much too bright and attractive to spend his life milking cows and planting corn. She felt certain that somehow, some day, Leonard would find a way to leave the farm and make something of himself. There had to be a niche in life for him. Somewhere.

That spring, another big change was about to happen in the life of Ida. She discovered she was in a family way and called Florence to break the news.

"That's really exciting," Florence said. "You say the baby is due in July? Do you think you'll still be able to attend a spelling contest this spring? Tillie Thomason has asked me to be the chairman for Six Mile Grove. Two other districts are competing and I thought you could help me. You've been saying you feel so left out of things now. The spelldown is the end of March."

There was a noticeable pause from Ida. "I'm not sure how Rudolph would feel about my going out in public, when I'm that far along. I might be showing by then."

"Ida, that's so old fashioned."

"Maybe so. And maybe you will understand about husbands when you get married yourself, someday. I don't want to stir up a problem with Rudolph over a spelling contest. Now let's talk about the chances for your team. Mabel Johnson always was my star student at District 88. She's your best bet to win a prize."

Florence hung up the telephone, feeling more than a little disappointed. Ida had changed so much, now that she was married. She always had to cater to Rudolph and what he thought. Did husbands always have to have the last word? She thought of the married women she had known quite well—Aunt Caroline, Aunt Oline, Emma Peterson and Britha Hanson. All of them had given up any spark of independence. But on the other hand, the fate of a spinster like Minnie Knudson or Dora Hanson was even worse. Whoever said it was a man's world was certainly right on target.

It was a hard winter that year. The temperature stayed below zero and roads were impassable most of the time. The little schoolhouse turned into an icebox. Florence always arrived early to light the fire in the coal stove, but sometimes the blackboard stayed frozen until noon. Snow blew under the front door and right through cloakroom, to lie in drifts on the classroom floor. The children sitting near the stove would get overheated while others near the edge of the room, would shiver with cold. Ever on the alert for frostbite or signs of lethargy in her pupils, Florence would announce it was exercise time. She would start some brisk jump-ups, to get the circulation going.

During these frigid winter weeks, Florence began tutoring sessions with Mabel Johnson, a Sixth Grader, along with a few other promising students. Mabel excelled in both spelling and arithmetic and jumped at the chance to get special attention. Florence's thoughts often drifted back to her sessions with Ralph Huston at District 34. Had it all been worthwhile? Had he managed to stay in school? Would he graduate this June? It was a hard fact that few farm boys ever got that far.

It seemed winter would never end. Leonard invited her to a few more dances and to the roller rink, but he never called on her like a real beau. This was like a friendship that was more than just a friendship, although Florence realized that no respectable man would court a young lady in a serious way, when he couldn't offer her anything. That simply wasn't done. And so Florence remained in a quandary that seemed to have no solution.

In the end, Rudolph put his foot down about Ida. He wouldn't allow her to travel out to Six Mile Grove in her delicate condition, so Ida wasn't there to see Florence conduct her first district spelling bee, and missed watching Mable qualify for the county competition. All Ida could do was stay home and read about it in the *Rural School Notes,* and feel impressed about the twenty-eight dollars Florence had raised at the box social. That remarkable sum would be donated toward the cash prizes for the big day in June.

Actually, Ida had felt too grieved to go anywhere. The death of her good friend, Jenny Hanson, hit her very hard. Jenny, who had hosted Ida's wedding ceremony, died of pneumonia, the scourge of so many young people according to the *Benson Review.* Nothing could be done to save them.

News of another death reached Florence. Clara, her older sister, wrote that Grandfather Thompson had died at the age of 80. Clara and Grandfather had become so close when they were homesteading together out in Bowman County, and Clara felt devastated. The funeral would be held in the spring when the ground thawed but of course, a trip to North Dakota was out of the question. It just seemed impossible to save money for anything.

Spring finally arrived and Julia Hanson rose from her sick bed, completely recovered from whatever it was that had ailed her. Now Julia took over the care of her baby and thought it was high time to take her turn in entertaining the Ladies Aid. One afternoon when Florence came home from school, she could hear the buzz of women's voices in the parlor. Hoping to slip past unseen, she made a beeline for the staircase. Then she heard a commanding voice call her name.

"Oh, there you are, Miss Thompson. Come in here for a moment. I have something to say to you."

With a sinking heart, Florence realized the voice belonged to the new Mrs. Lars Kvam—Betsy Offerdahl Kvam, Leonard's stepmother. The new wife was eleven years younger than Lars, very prim and self-possessed, the mother of the four Offerdahl children now enrolled at District 88. Florence stepped into the parlor to see the other ten ladies eating cake from Julia's best china plates. Now they stopped, as if alerted to an exciting new bit of gossip. From under the brims of their elaborate hats, all the eyes were fixed on the young schoolteacher.

"I hear that you are seeing Leonard Kvam," said Betsy in an accusing way. She wore a black bombazine dress and a big black hat with a matching feather that swept under her chin.

"I wouldn't call it *seeing* him in the usual meaning of those words. We've been roller-skating a few times."

"Well . . . you certainly wouldn't want to *marry* him." Betsy paused, her voice radiating disapproval. "That man is so lazy. All he wants to do is read, read, read. Just mark my words. He never will amount to anything."

A knot of rebellion began to twist in Florence's stomach, the same kind of rebellion she had experienced with H.R. Hanson and his rigid disapproval. What right did this woman have to call her into the parlor in front of the entire Ladies Aid, and ask such personal questions.

Julia Hanson put down her fork. "My Henry tells me that Leonard is a regular cigarette fiend. Imagine that! He'd better not try to smoke in *my* parlor."

Florence drew herself up as straight as possible. It was true that Leonard had started to smoke cigarettes. A lot of young men had taken up the habit but Leonard was not a fiend and he never, ever, had set foot in Julia's precious parlor. All of Florence's sensibilities told her this was the moment to say something tactful, anything to stay in the good graces of these women who had children attending her school. She had side-stepped dozens of questions before about her personal life, but this time . . . this time Florence felt a rising sense of outrage.

"I don't plan to marry Leonard or anyone else, for that matter," she said with a lift of her head, looking Betsy squarely in the eye. "But since you are so interested, I don't believe that Leonard is lazy. He works very hard, reading books to improve himself. He likes to study and learn."

"Study and learn!" Betsy folded her arms across her high-necked, black-fronted bosom. "Leonard is twenty-one years old! He has been out of school for years now. First he spent his father's hard-earned money going to that academy in Willmar, and then he made a fool out of himself trying to sell trinkets to stores. It's high time for Leonard to make himself useful."

Florence stood even straighter. "Don't worry about that. Leonard *will* make himself useful. *When* he is ready."

She turned on her heel and headed for the staircase. Once safely in her room, she found a handkerchief and began to blot the tears from her eyes. She felt like screaming but she had to calm this storm of pent-up emotions. How could that woman be so insensitive? So lacking in compassion? Now she could understand as never before, Leonard's valiant, if fruitless, effort to leave home. Penniless as he was, she felt that somehow Leonard would find a way to carve out a career for himself that would make everyone proud.

The following Sunday afternoon, Florence heard the sound of horse's hooves coming up the lane. She looked out the window to see Leonard dismounting, dressed in an overcoat and wearing his city hat. Anyone else would have worn clothes more suitable for riding but not Leonard. He always managed to break the mold. Florence grabbed a jacket and dashed outside to intercept him on the front veranda.

"Leonard! What a surprise!" He looked so handsome as always, but there was a serious expression on his face.

"I came over to tell you something, Florence. I'm leaving again."

"Leaving? Not on the road again, I hope."

"No. Never again. I read an advertisement in the newspaper about jobs for road builders out in North Dakota. I've heard a lot of young fellows are going out there. The pay is good and I'll have the chance to save some money."

"Does this have anything to do with all the nagging at home?"

"Partly. But I have to admit that Betsy is right. I should be on my own at my age. It's time for me to move on." He paused. "But I certainly will miss you."

Leaving again! Florence felt she might dissolve in tears, but she put on her bravest face. "I'm sure you know what's best. I wish you all the luck in the world. . . I'll miss you, too."

He reached for her hand and raised her fingers to his lips. "If I write to you, Florence, will you answer?"

"Of course I will." She forced a smile. "Let me hear from you just as soon as you are settled somewhere."

For one wild moment, Florence felt he might sweep her into a warm embrace, and give her a passionate kiss. But he stepped back, to give her one last yearning look. Then he mounted the horse and waved farewell. She watched the horse and rider trot down the lane, feeling a vast emptiness. So many things had been left unsaid. North Dakota was an entire world away, a desolate land of endless prairie, a place where the homesteaders could barely manage to stay alive according to letters from Clara. When Leonard reached the little wooden bridge, he turned to wave once more. Then horse and rider trotted out of sight. She stood motionless on the veranda, wondering if she ever would see Leonard again.

The days were filled with classes and coaching Mabel and her other students for the county competition. Either Adolph or Henry Hanson picked up the mail at the post office in town, but nothing arrived from North Dakota. Then about a month after Leonard's sudden departure, Henry handed a letter to Florence. "Looks like this one is for you."

Florence flew up to her room and savored every word. He had found a boarding place in Minot with a young couple named Cottington, and enclosed the address for her reply. He seemed to be well and happy, although the job was much harder than he had expected. Building roads definitely was not for weaklings. He signed the letter "Missing you." She sat right down to answer and signed her letter the same way.

The spring term was almost at an end when Tillie Thomason called on the telephone with a surprising request. "I know you don't have any students graduating this time, Florence. But I wonder if you plan to attend the exercises on June 2nd." It was true that Florence didn't have any students ready to graduate. Orin had dropped out again because of spring planting season.

"Of course I'm going. I wouldn't miss graduation. And I have some pupils entered in the county competition that morning."

"That's good. I'm putting a graduation program together and I wonder if you might be kind enough to sing a solo."

Florence hesitated. She never had sung at anything so big as a county graduation exercise. "Is anyone else going to sing?"

"One trio and one other vocal solo. Genieve Parker will play the piano. She always does at these programs. Do you have anything ready? There won't be much time for you to practice with her."

"Well, there's my old standby—In the Dark, In the Dew. But maybe that one is a little too sentimental for a graduation ceremony."

"The song sounds perfect to me, Florence. Thank you so much."

During all these preparations, Florence waited eagerly for the mail. Leonard wrote every week about how busy he was, adding to his bank account. Florence wrote about how busy she was, but didn't mention that her bank account looked flatter than the proverbial pancake, with barely enough for summer school. Then a letter arrived from Bernice in Fargo. She had a good-paying job at the telephone company now, and she could arrange to get Florence a similar position. She could make some good money and not throw her savings away on summer sessions at Moorhead. Florence could move in with Emily and Bernice. They were still rooming together.

Florence felt pulled in two directions. She loved going back to the Normal, but Bernice was right. She wasn't getting anywhere financially, and living with Bernice and Emily would be fun. She decided to head for Fargo right after graduation.

This time, the last day of school was just routine, since Tillie had asked her to come back to District 88 in the fall. The only worry on Florence's mind concerned the dirt roads. The spring rains had turned them into stretches of mud. When Rudolph came to pick up Florence and her trunk, to spend the night at the Johnson home, he wondered if they would make it back to Benson.

"I don't know when I've seen such a mess," he said, helping her into the buggy. "I wonder if all the folks can get to town for the big day tomorrow." The gooey mud clung to the carriage wheels and once they were underway, the horse continued to slip and slide as the buggy swayed and bounced along.

"I sure hope Mabel and the others can get there. I've put in a lot of work with those kids."

"Well, at least we can celebrate your birthday before

you leave for Fargo. It's June third, isn't it? How old are you going to be? Or aren't you telling."

"You know very well that I'll be twenty-two. It just doesn't seem possible that I've been teaching for four years."

"It sure doesn't," he agreed. "And it doesn't seem possible that pretty soon, I'm going to be a father."

The buggy made it to Benson at a very slow walk and that evening, Florence asked Ida to play the piano, so she could practice *In the Dark, In the Dew* one more time.

"Land sakes, you could sing that song backward," Ida said. "I'm sure you and Genieve will do just fine. I only wish Rudolph would let me attend. But you know how he is about that."

The next day dawned clear and bright, without a rain cloud in sight. Right after breakfast, Florence picked her way through the muddy streets to the high school. Fifty-four county schools would be represented that morning in the competition, and that meant a multitude of people would be there. But when Florence arrived, she saw only a thin scattering of wagons and carriages.

"Where are Tom and Mary and the others?" Florence asked, when she found Mable and her parents near the front door.

"They couldn't come, Miss Thompson," Mabel said, looking very demure in her low-waisted jumper and blouse. Long sausage-like curls hung to her shoulders, giving testimony to her mother's patience in rolling up the strands of blond hair in rags the night before, and tying each curl in a knot. "The roads are so terrible, we were lucky to get here. My pa had to dig the wagon out of the mud twice."

"Well, I guess it's up to you, Mabel, to carry the banner for District 88. Probably a lot of other people can't get here, either. And the competition won't be so stiff."

They found seats in the auditorium and settled down for a long wait, amid a rustle of whispering. Memories flooded back as Florence watched the pupils from the various schools take turns in the spelldown front of the podium, memories of Ralph and Alta and her very first spelling competition as a teacher. The Huston children were not entered in today's competition and Florence wondered if Ralph would graduate. Only sixty-two girls and thirty-seven boys would graduate that afternoon from the Eighth Grade, according to the *Benson Review*. To Florence, that seemed a sad showing for an entire county.

Then the Sixth Grade contestants were called to the podium. Florence squeezed Mabel's hand and wished her luck. "Be sure to smile at the superintendent, and curtsey first."

Florence watched Mabel head for the stage, sausage curls bouncing, and felt certain her star student should find this competition easy as pie. At least half the contestants hadn't been able to get there. Mabel carried on like a little trooper and spelled almost all the hard words correctly, before returning to her seat. "I just know I'm going to win something," Mabel grinned. "Thanks for helping me, Miss Thompson."

Grade by grade, there were so many categories it took about fifteen minutes for Tillie to call out all the winners and award the cash prizes. Florence had ears for only one name and at last she heard it: "Mabel Johnson, Fourth Prize for spelling in the Sixth Grade Division."

Mabel raced up to the stage to collect her one-dollar

prize. A little later, her name was called again, and Mabel returned to collect Third Place in the written composition division. One dollar and a half.

"I've never had so much money in my life," crowed Mabel when it was all over. "Thank you again, Miss Thompson."

After a picnic lunch with Mabel and her parents on the grounds of the high school, Florence made her way through the crowd, heading back to the auditorium. More parents and relatives were starting to arrive and band members in their bright blue uniforms, were starting to assemble. Off to one side, Florence spotted the line up of graduates dressed in their Sunday best, waiting to enter. She moved closer for a better look and then she saw him. Ralph Huston. He was taller now, more like a budding young man, and he was laughing and chatting with his companions. Picking up her skirts, Florence hurried to his side.

"Ralph! Congratulations! Somehow, I always knew that you would stay in school and graduate."

Ralph, suddenly bashful in front of the others, gave her a shy smile. "Hello, Miss Thompson."

"Tell me, what are your plans? Are you going to high school? You always were one of my best students."

A clouded look came into his eyes. "I wish I could, but my folks need me on the farm. I don't know anyone in town to board with and even if I did, it would cost too much."

Florence felt a stab of regret. This was such an old story. No place to board in town. No money for the farm children to go on to school.

"I'm so proud of you, Ralph. It's quite a feather in your cap, to graduate from the Eighth Grade. I just know you will do very well in life."

Ralph swallowed hard and blinked back a tear. For a brief moment, he looked so much like the Fifth Grader she remembered on that last pitiful day at District 34. "I'll never forget you, Miss Thompson. You're the best teacher I ever had."

"Thank you, Ralph. I'll never forget you either." She knew a hug would be out of place so she smiled and hurried into the auditorium. The high school band was on stage, tuning up in a chorus of dissonant sounds. Florence found a seat near Genieve who sat in serene confidence at the piano, her gray hair swept up in a pompadour, an opal brooch pinned to the high neckline of her dress. The band director, looking smart in his natty cap and gold braid, raised his baton for silence. The room fell into a hush and then the majestic sound of the *Triumphal March* filled the crowded room. The ninety-nine graduates entered in a slow dignified pace, walking in single file, to take their places in the front rows.

Florence glanced again at the program. She would be the third one to perform and she felt a sudden rush of nervousness. Then just as quickly, it faded away. Life was so good. . .Ralph Huston was about to graduate and Mable had won two prizes. This day was like a shining moment, one that made all the effort worthwhile. She really loved being a teacher.

She settled back in her chair, lost for a moment in a daydream. It should be easy to learn how to plug those long telephone lines into a switchboard. If Bernice could do it, she certainly could. In no time at all, she could afford to buy a train ticket to Rhame, to visit the family before school started again. She had looked very carefully on the map to find that little speck of a town in Bowman

County. It looked terribly far from Minot. About 200 miles.

Florence came back to earth with a jolt. Two hundred miles! She would need to ask about that long, impossible distance in her next letter to Leonard. He was writing so faithfully now and perhaps somehow, someway, he could manage to come all that distance for a visit.

Florence in a pensive pose.

Chapter Twelve

Bowman County, North Dakota
1916

Y ou have to like pioneer life to live out here," said
Robert Skare (SKAR-ee) as his wagon bumped over
the dirt road, heading for his homestead.

Florence felt as if her bones had been jarred down to
her toes, as if she would turn into a pool of sweat under
the relentless North Dakota sun. The vast prairie surrounded her—pastureland the color of brownish green,
barren and endless, pocketed with gopher holes and
without a single tree in sight. She looked up at her handsome brother-in-law with a mixture of admiration and
pity. He looked so strong and capable but how could he
hope to earn a living for Clara and his little girls on land
such as this?

"I'll take Minnesota any day," Florence replied. "I like
apple orchards and lakes and green fields. I don't know
why so many of the Thompson clan moved out to this
wilderness."

First there had been Clara and Grandfather, then her
brothers Wallace and Tom, then Isabelle with Mildred
and Kermit in tow, the youngest members of the family.

Clara and her grandfather, Thomas Thompson. Their claim shanty near Rhame, N.D. About 1910.

What they all saw in this dreary place was beyond her comprehension.

"The reason is free land, Florence. This is the last place in America where you can stake out a claim for 160 acres. We might not get rich this way, but we can call our homestead our own."*

Florence kept her thoughts to herself. She liked Robert so much—he was such a pleasant, easy-going man and she didn't want to hurt his feelings. It had been five long years since she had seen her oldest sister and now she could hardly wait until they arrived

---

*Under the Homestead Act of 1862, homesteaders could claim up to 160 acres so long as they lived on the land for a minimum of five years, farmed the land and did not try to use it for speculation.

"How did your visit with Isabelle go?" Robert squinted into the sun from under the broad brim of his rancher's hat. Robert was a cattleman, not a sheepherder like most of his neighbors. "Your mother is quite something. Not at all like Clara. Or you either."

Florence had just come from Isabelle's little rented house in Rhame, a duty visit that had gone fairly well. "Mother has a good sense of humor and I think that's where Clara gets it. But Mother can be cross as a bear, too. It seems I never can do anything to please her. At least she was glad I'd earned a little money at last, in spite of feeling bored stiff at the telephone company. Believe me, those girls work hard for their money. But I'd rather be teaching. Any day."

"Here we are," Robert said, turning his team onto a rutted lane. Up ahead, Florence saw a tiny sod hut held together with tarpaper, with a stovepipe sticking out of the rusted tin roof. There was a weather-beaten stable for the horses and a privy. A couple of leaning posts were planted in the bare ground in the side yard, obviously intended to hold a clothes line. Could this horrible-looking place be what her beautiful, fun-loving sister called home?

"Daddy, Daddy," called two little girls, as they ran to him from the side yard. They were Bea and Irene, just a year apart in age and too young for school. The shanty door flew opened and Clara dashed outside to greet them. She wore a long, gray, shapeless dress, her luxuriant hair piled up in a careless topknot.

"Florence! You're finally here! How well you look."

The stark change in Clara made words hard to find. Her thick wavy chestnut hair was showing touches of gray. Her slim figure had become stocky from childbearing, her complexion looked parched and dry as the prairie and Clara was not yet thirty. Florence had read about pioneer life and how hard it was on the women. Now she believed every word.

But Clara could still talk a blue streak as always, and she kept up a steady stream of chatter as she led Florence into the shanty. How was the visit with their mother? What was going on now in Fargo? And in Europe? Was the whole world going to war? Clara rarely had a chance to see a newspaper.

Florence felt claustrophobic in this tiny, low-ceilinged, dimly lit space. There was only one small window. Bare studs held the batten board walls together and overhead, bare rafters supported the roof. A small wood stove sat in one corner of the room, near a calico-covered couch that sagged in the middle. There was a small table with three wooden chairs. That completed the furnishings.

"Well, you can see we're roughing it," Clara said with a laugh. "But you should have seen the place before we fixed it up."

"You're just a crazy as ever," Florence said, relieved that Clara could still make a joke. Fix it up! This place was beyond hope. "You must have a bedroom. Somewhere."

"Right here. But be quiet and don't wake the baby." Clara pushed open a wooden, crossbar door and Florence peeked into a tiny room just barely big enough for a double bed and a baby carriage, where six-month-old Ruth lay sleeping.

"What an adorable baby. And where do Bea and Irene sleep?"

"The couch makes into a bed. It's a little crowded

Clara and her Grandfather Thompson, About 1910

THOMPSON FAMILY 1916. Top Row: Left to right standing:
Bernice, Clara, Wallace, Florence, Tom. Bottom Row: Left to right:
Kermit, Isabelle, Mildred.

here, but not too bad when the weather is nice and the girls can play outdoors. But in the *winter* . . ." Clara rolled her eyes and laughed again. "Let's have some coffee and you can tell me all about what's going on the world. Do you have a whole string of suitors in Swift County?"

Florence took a chair at the table, thinking she would die if she had to live in such a god-forsaken place. This was the way people lived fifty years ago—in sod huts—the way Grandmother Betsy had lived as a bride. Why, Clara and Robert didn't even have a telephone.

"Look, Florence. I baked a chocolate cake, just in your honor. I still love to cook and Grandpa used to say I was the one who kept him alive through the terrible winters out here. When I married Robert, Grandpa had to give up our claim. He couldn't go it alone, so he moved in with us. I miss him so much. He was so wonderful and patient, especially when the little ones came along."

A little later, while they were still catching up on the family news, a timid knock sounded on the door. Clara went to greet a thin, bespectacled, middle-aged man dressed in overalls. Behind him followed Robert and the two little girls.

"Florence, I want you to meet a good friend of ours," Robert said, smiling as always. "Mr. Harold Saxvik. He's the superintendent of schools in Bowman County. Harold, this is Clara's sister, Florence Thompson. She's a school teacher in Minnesota."

"Is that right, Miss Thompson? You are a teacher?" Mr. Saxvik beamed at Florence as if she were an angel sent from heaven.

"That's right, Mr. Saxvik. I am."

"We homesteaders need a teacher just desperately,

Miss Thompson. The children in this district haven't had school for a year now. It's a hardship living out on the prairie, I know. So many of the young people from our North Dakota Normal schools don't want to come to Bowman County. But you . . . you of all people . . . must be interested in helping these poor children." Mr. Saxvik took a chair, not able to tear his gaze from Florence.

"I couldn't stay here to teach. That would be impossible. Besides, I have a Minnesota Certificate. I couldn't teach in North Dakota, even if I wanted to."

"Don't worry about the certificate. I can take care of that. Just think of these poor children, Miss Thompson. Growing up without an education." Mr. Saxvik looked close to tears and he took off his spectacles to wipe them.

"Please take the job," Clara broke in. "We've all missed you so much. The whole family has missed you. And in a couple more years, Irene will be ready for school. It would just break my heart, if we didn't have a school here."

"Please stay," Robert urged. "We need you so much."

"Stay, stay," said Bea and Irene in a little chorus.

"You could live right here," Clara added. "We're only four miles from the schoolhouse. We could be together again. Just like old times."

Florence's heart almost stopped beating. Live here? In this horrible shanty? With no privacy? No room of her own?

"I just couldn't, Clara. Four miles is too far to walk, for one thing. This couldn't possibly work out. Mr. Saxvik can find some other teacher to come."

"We could arrange a closer boarding place," Mr. Saxvik begged. "The Currans are only a quarter-mile from school. They are fine people and have a nice house. A nice, big frame house with three rooms. They would be only too glad to board the teacher. Please, Miss Thompson."

"But I've made other plans. My superintendent is expecting me back at District 88, at Six Mile Grove in Minnesota."

"The children here need you so much. There are plenty of teachers available in Minnesota." Mr. Saxvik leaned forward in his urgency. "There are only eight children enrolled at District 29. It would be an easy job. And the salary is $55 a month." He hesitated, as if knowing the small salary wouldn't do the trick. "I wish I could offer more."

Florence's heart dropped to her boots. That was less money than she could make at District 88. And only eight pupils? What kind of a job would that be? But still . . . in spite of all the drawbacks, the idea of being closer to her family held a strong appeal. And she would be a little closer to Minot. She wouldn't have to live in this horrible shanty, but in a nice frame house. Florence felt herself wavering. "Well, I haven't actually signed the new contract, as yet."

"Does that mean you will take the job, Miss Thompson? Oh, bless you. The children will be so excited to have a school again. I know you won't have any discipline problems." Mr. Saxvik looked radiant, as if his prayers had just been answered.

"Please stay with us for just a little while," Clara said. "Until the weather gets cold. Bea and Irene won't bother you at all. They're very quiet sleepers. I know they won't mind sharing the bed with you."

"It's your decision where you will live," Mr. Saxvik

said. "You can move to the Curran place whenever you want. They have an adopted nephew—Elvin Laurvik—and they are so eager to have him in school again. Elvin is thirteen and a very bright boy."

Florence struggled with her mixed emotions. She couldn't help but wonder if she hadn't been set up for this all-too-convenient visit from the superintendent. It could be the biggest mistake of her life, to take this job. How could she bear to live in this shanty for one day, much less a couple of months? Just the thought of sharing a bed with Bea and Irene was bad enough. And yet . . . and yet . . . the joy of sharing laughter with Clara again seemed to compensate for it all. Life had been lonely at the Hanson place, with Leonard gone and Ida married and busy with her own life.

"Well, all right then. I'll take the job. But under two conditions. I'll stay here just a short time, until the weather gets cold. And Robert will have to teach me how to ride horseback. Four miles is too far to walk."

Clara jumped up to hug her sister. Mr. Saxvik promised to return the next day, so Florence could sign the contract for District 29. He would provide the lesson plans and do everything possible to make her stay a pleasant one. Robert cheerfully went back to Isabelle's house that very afternoon to get Florence's trunk. It was all settled. But Florence felt some very grave misgivings.

The next day, Florence received her first and only lesson in horseback riding. She put on a pair of Robert's old trousers although they were several sizes too big, and

Florence mounted on Buster

pinned the waist together with giant-size safety pins. She put on a shirt of Robert's and her oldest pair of boots. Then she went to the stable yard to meet her brother-in-law, who stood next to a huge brown horse that looked a little overfed and plump around the middle.

"Are you ready, Florence? I want you to meet Buster. He's the most gentle horse I have. I used to use him for riding herd but now he's too old for that. Put your left boot in the stirrup here and swing yourself up. This is a Western saddle. Just as comfortable as sitting in a rocking chair."

Florence did as she was told and looked down to the ground. It seemed so far away, down there. The big leather saddle creaked and it didn't feel anything like a rocking chair, with her legs spread so wide apart. "I'm all ready," she said.

"I'm going to lead you around in a slow circle, so you can get the feel of it. Keep your heels down and hold the reins up high. That's right. Don't be afraid. Buster won't run away with you."

"I'm not afraid," Florence lied. The swaying, jerking motion of the horse beneath her made her feel terrified, as if she would fall off at any moment. But she had to learn how to ride. There was no choice in the matter.

"Do you feel ready now to try it alone?" Robert asked, after they had been around in a circle a few times. "Keep your knees close to Buster. Pull the reins to the right like I showed you. Make him turn. Try a little harder. You have to show him who is boss."

"I'll try it alone now." When she saw Robert's hand drop from the bridle, she felt a ripple of fear. But she relaxed the reins and let Buster move forward.

"Now pull hard on both reins, Florence. Make him stop."

Florence pulled hard and Buster stopped with a jerk. She relaxed the reins again and dug her heels in the stirrups. Buster moved forward again. She was beginning to get the feel of it.

"Now you need to dismount and get up on Buster a few times. I want you to feel comfortable about that. I won't be there to help you at the schoolhouse. It's a good thing the place has a stable. Some of the kids ride horseback to school."

Florence did as she was told, realizing this would be more difficult to do in a skirt. But she couldn't go to school in Robert's old trousers. She doggedly rode around in the circle a few more times, sitting up straight, holding the reins up high.

"You're doing just fine," Robert said with his genial smile. "Give me a minute and I'll saddle up my horse and ride over to the schoolhouse with you. I want to show you how to water Buster, once we get there."

Side by side, Florence and Robert walked their horses to the school. They took the main road, going the full four miles, and then returned on a different short-cut route across a field and along a dry creek bed.

"Are you sure you don't want to learn how to trot or gallop?" Robert asked on their way back home.

"Walking suits me just fine," she replied. "I don't expect to ever enter a rodeo. But I suppose I should learn how to saddle up Buster, in case you aren't around to do it."

"Don't worry, Florence. I'll be glad to do that. Before you know it, you'll turn into a fine horseback rider."

Florence felt like anything but an expert horseback rider when she arrived at school early on Monday. It was September 16, 1916, the opening day, and one she would never forget. She tied up Buster in the stable, pumped some water from the well as Robert had directed, and made sure the horse was comfortable before she went to inspect the schoolhouse. The design was much like the country schoolhouses in Minnesota except the bell tower was taller and more prominent in the front of the building, instead of sitting like a little cupola on the roof. Well-worn wooden steps led up to the front door set into the base of this bell tower, and there was sort of an anteroom that opened to the cloakroom. Florence guessed this must be extra shelter from the winter winds.

The prairie sun had stolen all the paint from the frame siding and had parched the dry dusty schoolyard. There was no playground equipment of any description. She unlocked the door with the key Mr. Saxvik had given her and after locating the broom, Florence began to sweep the floor around her teacher's desk and down the aisles of the wooden desks and around the pot-bellied stove. Another year, she thought. And this one promised to be very different.

She put the lessons for the day on the blackboard and promptly at nine o'clock, she went outdoors to call the children. All eight pupils were lined up at the door like shy little sheep. There were five little ones who would be the beginning readers, plus three older children who ranged in age from twelve to fourteen. That fit exactly with the enrollment list Mr. Saxvik had provided.

As the children filed into the classroom, the first thing that struck Florence was their rag-tag clothing. All the shoes were scuffed and worn. Every dress was patched and ill-fitting, made over in some way, and every pair of knickers had patches at the knee. Some of these patches were neat, some haphazard, some of the patches bordered on other patches. Only one boy stood out like a shiny new penny. He was dressed in a clean white shirt and a neat pair of gray knickers and wore new-looking, ankle-top shoes. She guessed he must be Elvin, the Curran nephew.

His family must be wealthy by Bowman County standards.

"Good morning, children. I'm your new teacher. Miss Thompson. Please take your seats and we will make assignments later." When they were all seated and quiet, she said to the biggest boy, "What is your name?"

"Alfred Soudnes, teacher. I'm in the Seventh Grade. I was in the Seventh Grade last year too, but we didn't have any school." Alfred looked to be about fourteen.

"Well, Alfred, it will be your duty to fill the water pail each morning. And to make sure that my horse gets enough water each day. Can you do that for me?"

"Yes, Miss Thompson." Alfred looked very pleased to be singled out for such an important task.

Next Florence led the opening exercises, which were the same in North Dakota as in Minnesota, and then conducted the state required fifteen minutes of hygiene class. On this particular morning, Florence explained the necessity of a Saturday night bath, even in winter, if a person wanted to stay healthy and strong and free of germs.

"The Sixth and Seventh grade pupils may begin the geography lessons I have outlined on the board, paying particular attention to the countries in Europe, especially Germany."

Elvin raised his hand. "Do you think we will end up fighting Germany, Miss Thompson? My uncle says President Wilson will never let that happen. He says a vote for Wilson in November is a vote for peace."

"I hope your uncle is right," Florence responded. "The situation in Europe is very complicated. We need to learn about Germany and why the Kaiser is making so much trouble over there. We can talk more about it when we study current events. For now, you study the geography lesson while I gather up the beginning readers."

Florence pulled the small chairs into a circle, wondering how she could explain the war to the children, when she knew so little about it herself. Clara and Robert didn't get the *Bowman Pioneer* and there wasn't much to learn from the *Weekly Reader*, the publication for school children. The ugly situation in Europe seemed a world away.

She settled down to learn the names of her beginners: Henry and Agnes Soudnes in the First and Second Grades; Herman and Clifford Johnson, brothers in the First Grade since one had been kept behind; and Goldie DeLong, age 8, who seemed light years ahead of the others and already knew how to read. Luckily, she had packed her phonics cards and not left them at the Hanson's, so now Florence began with A. It seemed so strange not to hear the sing-song voices of Swift County but instead, the voices of children who always had spoken English.

During the mid-morning break of fifteen minutes, Florence put the arithmetic lessons on the blackboard, one for the primaries and another for the advanced pupils. The children trooped back in to settle down for addition and subtraction. The lessons consumed the balance of the morning and by noon, Florence felt very, very hungry. She hadn't taken time for a big breakfast and now she was glad she hadn't protested too much, when Clara had insisted on packing three ham sandwiches in a lunch bag plus an apple and an extra piece of cake. Florence felt she could eat all that and then some.

"It's time to take your lunch pails outdoors," she instructed. "I want you to enjoy this warm weather as long as we can. We'll have enough lunches indoors this winter, I'm afraid."

She watched as Goldie and Elvin and the two Johnson brothers headed for the cloakroom door, and then she heard their happy shouts from the schoolyard. The four Soudnes children simply sat at their desks and looked at one another. Then they ambled over to the teacher's desk and lined themselves up like stair steps—Alfred, the eldest, then Ida, then Agnes, then Henry, the youngest. They watched with big round eyes while as Florence unwrapped her first sandwich. "Didn't you bring something to eat?" she asked.

All four shook their heads in a definite no. All the eyes focused on the ham sandwich Florence had laid on her desk, and then on the apple she produced from the lunch bag, and then on the pocketknife Clara had thrown in as an afterthought.

"Well, then. Since you didn't bring anything today, I can divide my lunch. But be sure to ask your parents to pack something for you tomorrow."

She pulled out the second ham sandwich and then the third, again feeling grateful that Clara had been so generous. She cut the sandwiches into equal pieces, then the apple and the two pieces of cake, and gave all these portions to the children. They licked up every crumb as if they never had seen food before.

"I just love having school again," Ida Saudnes declared after downing the last morsel. She was the most woebegone child of all, painfully thin, with lank brown stringy hair, dressed in a wrinkled cotton jumper that was too big for her, and had been turned up several times at the hemline. "We didn't have anything to do last winter."

"I love having school too," added Alfred, the water carrier. His hair was the same nondescript color as his sister's. There was a sprinkling of freckles across his broad nose and his eyes were set too close together, giving him a squinty look. The knees in his brown corduroy knickers sported big patches of denim.

"Me too," said Agnes, the Second Grader, a younger edition of Ida.

"Me too," said Henry, the First Grader. "Only I'm still hungry."

"I'm afraid that's all the food I brought today," Florence said. "Just remember about asking your parents to pack a lunch tomorrow." She had eaten nothing at all, and now her stomach was grumbling.

The Soudnes children edged away from her desk and went outside to play. They looked so desperately poor, Florence feared this same situation might continue to happen the next day, and perhaps for the balance of the term.

Later that afternoon, when she arrived back at the claim shanty, Florence told Clara about her experience at lunchtime. "I should speak to Mr. and Mrs. Soudnes myself. I couldn't very well reprimand the children, just because their parents are so careless."

"Fat lot of good that will do," said Clara, handing Florence a sandwich to tide her over until suppertime. "Mr. Soudnes is an itinerant preacher and the family lives in a shanty worse than this one. He doesn't have a penny to his name."

"But this isn't fair. And I can't eat with four pairs of hungry eyes staring at me and you can't afford to keep packing such big lunches."

"You'll just have to get tough, Florence. Like a real

pioneer. You have to look out for yourself, when you live on the prairie." There was a mischievous glint in Clara's eye. She always could make a joke of everything, but this wasn't a laughing matter.

The next day, Clara packed six sandwiches, more than one person could possibly need, and that made Florence feel guilty. Clara and Robert were barely subsisting as it was, and they couldn't afford to feed that hungry brood. She would just have to give Clara a little extra money for her room and board. It was little wonder that Mr. Saxvik had so much trouble getting a teacher, so long as the Soudnes children were enrolled at District 29.

September melted into October and into November, while Florence and Clara continued to deal with the school lunch problem. Robert picked up the mail whenever he was in town and there were always letters from Leonard. He wrote he had felt very proud to cast his vote for Woodrow Wilson that year on the Democratic ticket. The Peace Candidate. It had been a narrow victory in the Electoral College over Charles Evans Hughes, a man who proved to be petty, antagonistic and quarrelsome according to some of the editorial writers.

Florence fell into the habit of staying longer at school, to keep up with her letter writing and to postpone her return to the noisy and crowded claim shanty. Leonard was doing such exciting things now that the roadwork season was over. He had found a job as a teller at the Minot bank and in the evenings, he did bookkeeping for the Minot Garage. There was so much to write about!

Thanksgiving was approaching. One November day after class, Florence began working on a special program to honor that event, and stayed at school extra late to cut out some material to make Pilgrim dolls. Darkness began to settle when she started on the road for home. She could feel the frigid air begin to creep through her long underwear, and gave Buster a little kick to urge him to go faster.

The horse whinnied in alarm. He darted forward, lost his footing, and the next thing Florence knew, she was falling to the ground in a crash of hooves and leather. Buster had slipped on a patch of ice, lost his rider and then pranced off a short distance. Florence discovered she had skinned her knee but she hobbled over to Buster and began to stroke his velvety nose. Once he had quieted down, she re-mounted and began the slow chilly ride for home, with her knee throbbing and spirits disheartened.

"I think it's time for me to move to the Curran place," Florence said that evening at supper, after telling about her mishap. "It's getting so cold now and that was the agreement."

"Can't you stay a little longer," Clara begged. "It's been so much fun having you here. Just like old times."

It was true the sisters had become close companions again, laughing at Clara's jokes, doing laundry at night while the children slept, baking cookies that never seemed to turn out right in the uneven heat of the coal stove. Whatever the task, Clara made it fun. All this made it difficult to leave.

"Honestly, Clara. I can't stay any longer. The road is too icy. Please ask Robert to help me move on Saturday."

"All right. But on one condition. That you will come back in the spring."

"In the spring," Florence agreed, although she was filled with more than a few reservations. It would be hard to go back to the sod hut and have to share her bed again with two wiggly little girls. She never had unpacked, since there was no place to put her things, and living out of her trunk had been far from enjoyable. Now Florence looked forward to living in a real house again with windows and some comfortable furniture. She didn't dare hope there might even be a room of her own.

Chapter Thirteen

The Curran Place

"I hope you will be comfortable here," Sarah Curran said with a gracious smile, after Robert had departed in his wagon. "It means so much for Elvin to have school again. I tried to tutor him at home last year, but that didn't work out too well. I had trouble keeping up with the school-work myself."

"I enjoy having Elvin at school, Mrs. Curran. He is by far my star student." Florence meant that from the heart. Any teacher loves to have a student like Elvin—bright, eager to learn and always helpful. He had all the advantages of a well-loved youngster, whereas the Soudnes children were so pitiful and neglected, they were like characters out of a Charles Dickens novel. The Johnson brothers were good students and so was Goldie, who knew all the phonics cards by heart. But Elvin was special.

"Please call me Sarah. I don't like to stand on formality, and I want us to become good friends. Don't worry about using our parlor as your bedroom. The sofa makes into a bed and there is a closet where you can hang up your dresses. The rest of your things will have to stay in your trunk, I'm afraid. There isn't space for an extra bureau."

Sarah Curran looked exactly like a typical pioneer—

wiry, plain and down-to-earth—someone who would turn a penny over a few times before she spent it. Florence guessed her age to be about forty-five.

"You probably know the story about Elvin," Sarah continued. "We took him in about six years ago, when his parents died of influenza. He is my husband's nephew. We had just finished building our new house at the time, so we kept the sod shanty and fixed it up for Elvin. That works out nicely, since it's attached to the house. Now let's go into the parlor. I want you to meet my husband, Charles. He had a stroke last year and has a little trouble speaking. But he's getting better now. Just be patient with him."

Florence followed Sarah into the other room, to meet the elderly man who sat in an overstuffed chair, reading a newspaper. He looked thin and gaunt, much older than his wife, with a chiseled face and shaggy gray eyebrows. His eyes were bright and alert, revealing a keen spark of intelligence.

"Hello, Miss Thompson. We are happy to have you here." Mr. Curran spoke in a slow, measured way and it wasn't hard to tell he was a man of genteel upbringing.

"I'm very happy to be here," Florence replied. The parlor was austere and simple, with a three-cushion sofa. Lace curtains hung at the windows and there was a round mahogany table covered with a crocheted doily and a cluster of family photographs. "And who is this?" she asked, picking up a silver-framed portrait, a picture of a handsome and studious-looking young man.

"Our son, Anthony," Sarah replied. "He lives in New York. Anthony is a writer and he is published in several magazines there."

"A writer! How wonderful. Does he ever come to visit?"

"Not very often," Mr. Curran said sadly. "But he writes to us every week. Anthony is very well educated. He went to college in New York City for a while. I will let you read his next letter."

"That would be very kind, Mr. Curran." Florence reflected on how fortunate she was to live in a real house again, and with such friendly, nice people.

Later that afternoon, when Florence joined Sarah to help in the kitchen, she heard a loud knock on the door, followed by a gale of childish giggles. She saw her land-lady stiffen and purse her lips.

"Oh dear." Sarah heaved a sigh. "I know who that is. The Soudnes children, come a-begging again. They must about drive you crazy at school, Florence. They are my brother's kids, I'm ashamed to say. They're always over here, making pests of themselves. But this time, I'm not giving them a thing. Not a thing."

Sarah went to open the kitchen door and on the steps stood the entire Soudnes clan—the four Florence knew from school and three younger ones, one hardly more than a toddler.

"We're so hungry, Aunt Sarah," said Alfred with a doleful look. "Can't you spare a little something? Ma and Pa should be home from preaching in a few more days."

"And they won't be bringing any groceries with them, will they? I know all too well, how it goes with them." Sarah's tone was sharp and angry.

"Please, Aunt Sarah." Ida Soudnes twisted the hem of her shabby coat. Her pathetic expression reminded Florence of the daily scene around her desk at school. Still, her heart melted at the sight of all this neglect. The toddler, dressed in a dirty jacket that was much too big for him, began to cry. Agnes followed suit, and then Ida.

Sarah put her hands on her hips. "Well, this is positively the *last* time. You children should have tended your garden last spring, the way I showed you. Lord knows, I planted the seed myself—carrots, potatoes, squash—just everything you could possibly need. I told you to keep the garden watered, if you wanted to eat this winter. And now look. Stay on the porch. I don't want you tracking up my kitchen."

Sarah opened the door of her vast pantry with its shelves of home-canned vegetables, and heaved another sigh. She reached into her larder where she kept the smoked meat, and found a package of salt pork wrapped in cheesecloth. She put that into one of the outstretched hands. Grumbling to herself, she added a loaf of her home-baked bread and a Mason jar filled with green peas.

"Now mind you, children. You start digging some lignite and get ready for the cold weather. I don't want to hear about your father burning his fence posts for fuel, the way he did last winter."

The children scurried off with their loot while Florence felt compelled to ask a question. "Do you mean their father was too lazy to dig lignite?" The area was rich in lignite and everyone dug the coal, free for the taking.

"Even for that. The man is impossible but burning his fence posts was just the limit. Of course, come spring, he was over here wanting to borrow some money to buy new fence posts. Did you ever hear of such a thing?"

Florence had to admit as much. She never had known a family like the Soudnes. The situation reminded her of the fable about the ant and the grasshopper, the one she often read to the children at story time. The ant worked all summer to store up food while the grasshopper made fun of the ant, and played and enjoyed himself. But when winter arrived, the grasshopper came knocking on the door of the anthill, begging for something to eat.

It was easy enough for the ant to say *no*, and scold the grasshopper for being so foolish. After all, he was only a grasshopper. But it was not so easy for Sarah to say *no* to her own flesh and blood when they came begging for food. And not so easy for Florence to say *no* when the children crowded around her desk at lunchtime. It seemed a predicament that could not be resolved.

"I don't like to ask you, Sarah, since I know how you feel about this. But the Soudnes children rarely bring a lunch pail to school. So do you think you could pack a little extra for me, so I can share? My sister Clara did it, when I was staying with her, and I gave her a little extra for my room and board."

Sarah hesitated, a grim expression on her face. "The last teacher who boarded here had the same trouble. But I don't want to take any extra money. You get paid so little as it is. So I guess I can pack bigger lunches but that really is against my principles."

Elvin came into the kitchen just then, to see what the commotion was all about, and Florence was struck with a new idea.

"How would you like to be my janitor at school, Elvin? It would be worth a dollar a week to me, if you would go to school a half-hour early to build a fire in the coal stove. It would be so wonderful to come to a nice warm schoolhouse, and not have to do that job myself anymore."

"A dollar a week! Gee, Miss Thompson. That's too much money just to build a fire."

"It's worth it to me. If you don't feel right about the dollar, then you could clean the blackboard and sweep the floor too. How about it?"

Elvin agreed that he would like the job. Florence wished with all her heart that she could have offered the job to Alfred Soudnes, who needed the money much more than Elvin. But she knew from experience she couldn't depend upon Alfred. He often forgot to fill the water pail or see about Buster, and Alfred almost never got his homework done on time. Alfred was like the grasshopper in the story, and just like his father when it came to taking responsibility. On the other hand, Elvin was industrious, just like his aunt Sarah.

The weeks flew by, highlighted by the mail delivery and letters from Leonard. Three times a week, one of the sheepherders in the area would pick up the pouch of mail left by the rural carrier at an abandoned claim shanty, four miles from Rhame. Then the volunteer would make the rounds to deliver the mail to his neighbors, usually after the evening chores were done. The husky ranchers worked out a schedule for this important task but because of his frail health, no one expected Charles Curran to take a turn. The Curran mail was delivered anyway.

Florence came to associate the sound of horse's hooves with the evening mail delivery, and she didn't mind all the teasing from the sheep ranchers. They always read the postcards and every word on an envelope including the postmark. "Looks like there's another important letter from Minot," the rancher would say with a grin, before handing it over. "That feller sure is faithful."

This was like an evening ritual. Mr. Curran would draw up a chair to the kitchen table and offer the circuit rider a cup of coffee. Then they would exchange some local gossip or argue about politics and whether President Wilson should negotiate with the Germans or not. Whenever a letter came from Anthony Curran, the rider would deliver that one first. Mr. Curran would open the envelope with slow deliberation and real aloud in his halting way, all about the latest doings in the far away world of New York City. The rider always stayed to hear every word, while Florence and Sarah sat enthralled. They all agreed that Anthony had a way with words.

Sometimes Florence would share parts of her letter with the Currans. Leonard's job at the bank was going well, and he was learning a lot about these new style motor cars from his bookkeeping work at the Minot Garage. Leonard was impresssed with the way people scrimped and saved to buy an automobile, and then spent even more to keep it running. One rich man in town had a Packard and a chauffeur to drive it.

Florence always had a letter ready for the circuit rider to take along in his mail pouch, to leave for the regular carrier. In her letters to him, she could pour out her hopes and frustrations in a way she never could do with anyone else. She felt so isolated on the prairie and wanted to know everything that was going on in the bustling city of Minot. She signed her letters with "Love" even though this didn't seem like a real romance.

Meanwhile, Florence announced her plans for a Christmas program, the first one ever to be held at District 29.

"You mean we're going to have a *boughten* tree!" Alfred Soudnes looked astounded when he heard the news.

"You mean a tree bought from a store," Florence corrected. "I have to buy a tree because there are no trees around here. We can't go out and just cut one down, the way we could in Minnesota. I want everyone to bring cranberries and popcorn tomorrow. We can start to make strings to decorate the tree."

"We don't have any cranberries in North Dakota," Elvin objected.

"Well, that's right. I'll get some colored construction paper when I go to town and we can make paper chains instead."

"I've never seen a real Christmas tree," Henry Soudnes crowed with delight. The others admitted they never had seen a Christmas tree either. No one questioned where the money would come from, and Florence didn't mention the school board had turned down her request for funds. It looked like Christmas would have to come out of the teacher's pocket again.

At home that afternoon, Florence asked Sarah for use of the wagon, so she could go to town for the tree. She'd read in the *Bowman Pioneer* that some nice evergreens had been imported from Wisconsin and would be sold for reasonable prices.

"I think you might want to read this letter first," Sarah said. "The mail was early today and this letter just came from Minot. I don't want to be nosy, but it looks important."

Florence opened the letter and could hardly believe the words she read. Leonard was still a man of endless surprises.

Dearest Florence,

I would give anything to visit you for Christmas but that is impossible.

I'm too tied down at the bank But since you have a vacation, I wonder if you would like to come to visit me.

I have moved to the Waverly Hotel, so you could stay at the Cottington's house, the couple I used to board with and we are good friends. They have a nice room and would love to have you. Please come as soon as you can, and let me know which train to meet. I will pay you back for the train fare. Please say that you will come.

With all my love,
Leonard

Florence looked up from the letter, feeling dizzy with sheer happiness. "Sarah—Leonard has invited me to go to Minot for Christmas!"

She sat right down to write a letter of acceptance before leaving for town, where she could hurry and get it in the mail. The details about the time would have to wait until her next letter, and exactly when she could come. She knew she would have to spend Christmas at her mother's in Rhame, as she had promised. But she could leave right afterward. She couldn't wait to see him!

The excitement of it all carried her through the rehearsals and the Christmas program that featured the singing of the carols. The program was a huge success although she had yet to meet the most peculiar parents, Mr. and Mrs. Soudnes. They were off on another preaching mission. Florence gave an orange to each child and she received a tiny bottle of lilac-scented toilet water from the Johnson parents, a handkerchief from Goldie DeLong, and a week of free janitor service from Elvin

School was dismissed for the Christmas holiday and her brothers, Tom and Wallace, came to get her in their wagon. The brothers were homesteading together and barely managing to eke out a living. The three went to Isabelle's tiny house in Rhame, where they had a reunion with the youngest members of the family, Mildred and Kermit. It was all happening so fast, Florence had no time to prepare her mother about Leonard. She and Isabelle almost never had heart-to-heart talks like other mothers and daughters, and now she found it hard to bring up the subject. Florence waited until after supper, when the family was seated around the table and the atmosphere seemed jolly and peaceful. Then she casually mentioned her trip to visit Leonard Kvam right after Christmas, and how she would be staying at the home of his friends.

Isabelle stared across the table, her ample bosom heaving, her square-jawed face looking like thunder. "What! You mean you are going to traipse halfway across North Dakota to visit a man you hardly know!"

Mildred and Kermit stared at Florence with round eyes. Tom and Wallace tried to hide their smiles. They all knew about their mother's quick temper, and how it was best to fade into the shadows whenever she became riled up about anything.

"I've come to know Leonard very well through his letters," Florence replied with a lift of her head. "We've been corresponding for a long time now. He comes from a very

The Thompson Girls: Clara, Florence, Mildred, Bernice

respectable family and I'm sure you would like him. If you knew him."

"You are *not* going to chase after a man. I've never heard of such a thing. Young ladies do not go to visit young men. If you did such a terrible thing, your reputation would be ruined." Isabelle's strong jaw was set in a firm line.

"I'm not chasing after Leonard. He invited me. I will be well chaperoned. Leonard is living at a hotel now and I will be at the Cottington's house. Now what is so wrong about that?"

"You are much too headstrong, Florence. Always have been. First you want to go off to high school and work like a slave for Aunt Caroline, then you want to go to the Normal and fill your head with high-flown ideas. And now you want to flounce off to visit a man and ruin yourself even more. Don't you realize that no self-respecting man will want to marry you, after such an affair? Well, I forbid it. And that is final."

"Mother, I'm very sorry that you feel the way you do. But I am going to Minot. I can't see anything wrong about it. I know how to take care of myself. I've been doing it for a long time now. And you need to understand that."

Isabelle carried her dishes into the kitchen and started to crash about, scrubbing pots and pans with fury, slamming cupboard doors, while the little sister and the three brothers looked at Florence with newfound awe and respect. No one ever had stood up to Isabelle like that. But Florence seemed to get away with it.

The conflict cast a pall over the Christmas gathering and Florence was glad when the visit came to an end. Early on the day after Christmas, Tom stood ready to take her to the depot. Florence gave her mother a peck on the cheek. "Goodbye. I'll see you over spring vacation, if that's all right with you." She climbed into the wagon and waved farewell.

At the depot, Tom gave her a brotherly hug. "Have a good time, Sis. Ma will get over it. Maybe in a couple of years."

Florence didn't like to leave this way, with the troubles unresolved. But the desire to see Leonard after all this time, blotted out the family difficulties. She had to know in her own heart if this was true love, or just some will-o'-the-wisp dream born out of loneliness and her yearning to have a home of her own. This visit should settle those questions. At least she hoped it would.

Later that day, the train pulled into the station at Minot. From the window of her passenger car, Florence could see Leonard waiting on the platform, engulfed in a cloud of steam, a big bouquet of flowers in his hand. She caught her breath. Her heart beat a little faster. In a few more minutes, she was in Leonard's arms.

"My dear girl! I can't believe you're really here. You look so beautiful. I've missed you so much. You'll never know. Now I can't wait to show you the city and have you meet all my new friends. And where I'm working now. And everything."

The first strangeness of being together again, melted away. Leonard led her to the Model-T Ford he had rented just for the occasion, and they drove to the Cottington's house. On the way, as they talked about his new job and his new life in Minot, Florence could see how much he had changed. The old farm shyness was gone. He seemed such a man of the world now, so confident and sure of himself. She felt proud to be with him and obviously so important to him.

"Well, what do you think of Minot?" asked Norma Cottington, after Leonard had left for the hotel. "And what do you think of our little bungalow? It's the latest style now in city houses. Compact and quaint, so the salesman said."

"I'm still dizzy from all the excitement. I love your house. And I love Minot and the electric lights and automobiles buzzing around. Best of all, I love your indoor bathroom. That's a luxury I rarely have."

Norma laughed. She was just a few years older than Florence and seemed very modern and up-to-date. Norma wore a skirt that came to the ankle and mid-heel shoes instead of boots. She was very pretty and wore her dark hair in tight waves that covered her ears.

"This is your room, where Leonard used to stay when he lived with us. I'll give you a little time to freshen up. That must have been a long dusty trip on the train. I'm sure Leonard has told you about the big dinner party planned for tonight. It's going to be at the Waverly."

"Yes, he has. I can't wait to meet all his new friends."

"Florence, you are a lucky girl to have a man like Leonard. I think the world of him. He is so gentlemanly and kind to everyone and has a wonderful sense of humor. too. We loved having him here. I'll get your bath ready for you."

A few minutes later, Florence sat in the claw-footed tub, savoring the joys of hot running water and the use of a toilet that flushed by pulling the long chain that dangled from the water closet above. She gazed at the electric light bulb in the ceiling, and the oval mirror above the long-stemmed ceramic washbowl. It was all like a dream. But she wondered about Norma's remark. She didn't exactly have Leonard in the way Norma meant. He never had announced his intentions and yet they seemed made for each other. Was she taking too much for granted? Well, she would have an entire week to find out.

A little later, Leonard arrived in the Ford with Ed Cottington, a fine-looking young man who seemed full of fun. He was also employed at the bank and told Florence he was saving money to buy a motor car, and soon would no longer need to ride the trolley to work. Norma and Ed were childless, so they were free as birds to go off for an evening to enjoy themselves. They seemed a very modern and sophisticated couple.

"What do you think of the Waverly?" Leonard asked as they strolled into the lobby with its Oriental rugs and a huge electric-light chandelier that hung from the vaulted ceiling, paneled walls and stiff settees in appropriate places for elegant guests to sit and chat. Florence never had seen anything quite so overwhelming, not even in Fargo.

"It looks just like the picture postcard you sent. And so tall! Four stories."

"The rooms on the top floor are the cheapest ones," Leonard admitted. "It's quite a walk up but I don't mind it. I'd show you my room but I guess that wouldn't be proper."

Florence blushed. "I wish you could know how angry my mother was, that I came to Minot at all. She would simply die, if she ever thought I went to a man's hotel room."

"I don't want to get on the wrong side of your mother," Leonard said with his wry smile. "I hope to meet her, some-day."

Leonard led the way to the ballroom, to a long table covered with gleaming white linen where several couples were seated. He introduced Florence to everyone and she noticed the men were drinking wine, and several of the ladies too. They were all dressed in beautiful clothes, the men in handsome suits with padded shoulders; the women in slim beaded dresses like Norma's with ruffles around the necklines. Florence felt thankful that her dress was in the latest fashion too, thanks to Emily who always kept up-to-date.

A dinner of several courses was served, with waiters bobbing around to make sure the wine glasses were filled and the dishes cleared. Florence didn't drink any wine, fearing she might not like it after her one bad experience, but Leonard seemed to enjoy it. A live orchestra was seated at one end of the ballroom, with strings and a wind section and a concert grand piano, and the muted sounds of a waltz filled the air. Florence wished that Ida could see her now, in all this elegance and splendor. Ida would no longer think that Leonard was just a country boy, and not worth knowing at all.

"Would you like to dance," asked Leonard, after they had finished their parfaits served in tall fluted glassware. He led her to the dance floor and took her in his arms, just as smooth and nonchalant as if he had been dancing all his life. "I hope my dancing has improved a little, since that first night at the Town Hall."

"I guess I don't need to tell you this is the most exciting evening in my life. It will be very hard to go back to Bowman County and live like a pioneer again."

"Do you really think you could get to like city life?" Leonard looked amused. It was easy to see he enjoyed entertaining her. "Let's go back to the table for a few minutes. I have something to show you. A little Christmas present."

When they were seated again, Leonard reached into his pocket. He pulled out a little box that looked like it came from a jewelry store, and opened it. Inside was a silver ring with a tiny solitaire diamond set up on prongs, to make it look bigger. Florence stared. She could hardly breathe. "I don't know what to say. I couldn't be more surprised."

"Just say yes. You want to be engaged, don't you? I've loved you from the first moment we met, but I was too young. Too unsettled. Let's face it. Too poor. Now things are looking up for me." He took the ring out of the box and slipped it on her finger. "The problem is, we can't get married for a while. Not until I'm making more money. I just don't want one of those sheepherders you write about, to steal you away from me."

Florence leaned back in her chair, her head spinning. This was so unexpected . . . this ring . . . this proposal. But Leonard did unexpected things. That was part of his charm, part of what she loved about him. She knew that life with Leonard would never be dull.

"Yes . . . yes. We can wait about getting married. But you are so impetuous. You take my breath away."

"That's just how I am. I can't help it." He reached over to kiss her cheek. "Some day I'll get you a bigger ring. You can bet on it."

Suddenly, from the direction of the dance floor, came a loud shout. "Did she say *yes*?" It was Ed Cottington, making a megaphone of his hands. All the friends on the dance floor joined in a chorus of shouts. "Did she say *yes*?"

"She said *yes*," Leonard shouted back. Ed dashed over to their table and pulled Florence to her feet, while the orchestra played a snappy rendition of *Hail, Hail, the Gang's All Here*. Within moments, Florence found herself in the center of the dance floor with Leonard holding her hand, and all the friends circling them in a riotous snake dance. At first, it was just the companions from their table but soon, everyone in the ballroom joined in, laughing and singing. It was like a hundred New Year's Eves rolled into one.

"Now do you think this is the most exciting moment of your life?" Leonard pulled her closer, his face aglow with happiness.

"Absolutely." It was a night that Florence would always remember.

Later, after they had shared their first kiss on the Cottington's front porch, Florence felt compelled to ask a few questions. "You had everything staged so well this evening. With Ed and even with the orchestra. But what would you have done, if I had said no? Wouldn't you have been embarrassed?"

Leonard laughed. "I knew you wouldn't say *no*. A girl like you wouldn't come all this way to Minot, just to see an old friend. I could read between the lines of your letters. I knew you cared about me, just as much as I care about you. I'm a fairly bright fellow, you know."

Florence reached up to give him another kiss. He was a very bright fellow and worth waiting for. But even then, Florence had the feeling this might turn out to be a very, very long engagement.

It was a glorious week. Leonard had to work at the bank during the day, so Norma entertained Florence. She took her to see everything worth seeing in Minot. In the evenings, the two couples played whist or went dancing or visited friends. Florence never had been in such a social whirl. But all too soon, the week ended and it was time to board the train for Rhame. Saying goodbye to her handsome fiance´ was terribly hard to do. Florence wondered how she could face the long dreary months that lay ahead.

Florence and her pupils in the doorway of the school. Bowman
County, North Dakota.

Chapter Fourteen

Winter in North Dakota

Florence felt desperately lonely when she returned to the classroom routine. Kind as her landlords were and pleased about her engagement, Florence felt a need to be with young people her own age again. When a fellow-teacher, Velma Maynard, suggested going to a Teachers Institute at Bowman, Florence jumped at the chance. Bowman, the county seat, was only twenty-five miles from Rhame, just a quick train ride away.

"Are you sure you want to make this trip, Florence?" Sarah Curran asked early that Saturday morning while she was fixing breakfast. "I'm worried you might get caught in a snow storm. It's such a blustery day. More windy than usual."

Florence knew a North Dakota winter was not to be taken lightly. A blizzard could come up without any warning, and she had heard frightening tales about people getting lost in these sudden storms.

"It's such a short day trip and I'll be staying at the Maynard ranch tonight. Velma is so lucky to be able to live with her own family. Her brother Zindy, is going to meet us when we get back to Rhame. He will bring me back here Sunday afternoon. It's all arranged."

The sky was clear and the sun was shining when Mr. Curran took her to the depot in his sled. Florence looked forward to spending some time with Velma who was only nineteen and fresh out of the Normal. It didn't matter that the Institute would cover that same old material about the Palmer Method. There would be a lecture on current events and perhaps she could make some sense out of what was going on in the world. The last she'd heard, the Allies had announced the only outcome of the war in Europe had to be a complete defeat of the Central Powers. But Florence felt certain Charles Curran was right. The United States never would be drawn into that terrible conflict. Woodrow Wilson would keep his word about that.

The seminar was a wonderful diversion and the sun was just dropping out of sight when the train pulled into the depot at Rhame at five o'clock that afternoon. A light snow started to fall in thin wispy flakes and the temperature was dropping. "Look, there's Zindy," Velma called as they alighted from the train. She pointed toward a husky-looking youth wearing a red woolen scarf. He was dressed in boots and leggings, heavy jacket, a leather brimmed cap with earflaps tied under his chin. The girls hurried over to the family sleigh, drawn by a team of horses.

"Looks like we might have more snow than this," Zindy said as he scanned the darkening sky. "That shouldn't bother two strong girls like you. It's fifteen miles to home, so we'd better get going."

"We're going to freeze in this open sleigh," Velma said as she climbed into the back seat and wrapped her long coat around her.

"I brought the bearskin blanket, and I'll tuck you in. You girls should be just fine."

He mounted in the front seat and in a whirl of snow, they headed down a dirt trail that was narrow as a cow path. The snow continued to fall and by the time they had traveled a mile or two, the trail was almost obscured under a wind-tossed blanket of white.

"I don't know how Zindy can see where he's going," Florence said, feeling a little apprehensive. Darkness came so quickly on the prairie.

"Don't worry," Velma said. "Zindy knows this trail. He'll just keep bearing to the northwest and before you know it, we'll be home. If we don't freeze first." Velma burrowed deeper into the bearskin.

Florence felt the wind freshen, biting her cheeks and stinging her eyes. She wore a woolen cap pulled down over her ears, the woolen scarf and mittens that Grandmother had made, and her warmest long coat. Her boots had a flannel lining but her toes were beginning to tingle with cold. The last rays of the sun slipped below the horizon and now the snow came down in thick heavy flakes. Surrounded by fields of white, Florence couldn't see a trail at all. She heard the horses whinny in discomfort as the time dragged along and they seemed to be getting nowhere. An hour passed and then another hour. Florence felt a dreadful sense of unease. Something was not right. It shouldn't take this long to go fifteen miles.

Suddenly, the sleigh halted. Florence saw Zindy get out and start to lead the horses, trudging slowly into the darkness ahead. She watched him push forward with careful steps, his scarf blowing straight behind him in the fierce wind. Her unease turned into a sharp stab of fear. It was well known that sometimes the bodies of people lost in a blizzard never were found.

"I'm getting scared," Velma whispered. "I've never seen Zindy get out and walk like this, leading the horses."

"I'm scared too," Florence admitted. She hadn't seen a light anywhere since they had left town. They hadn't passed a single hut or shanty. She didn't dare to think what might happen next. They continued another quarter of a mile or so, and then Zindy struggled back to the girls, leaning close to their faces so they could hear his voice above the screech of the wind.

"I'm lost! I wasn't sure at first, so I got out to walk a little way. There's a gravel pit somewhere around here. I'm afraid to drive any farther. We might fall into it in the dark. The horses are tired, fighting this wind. But we've got to keep moving."

"Oh, Zindy! What can we do?" Velma sounded frantic with fear.

"We've got to keep going. We can't sit here and freeze. You two get out and walk. We're bound to find something, maybe a house, sooner or later."

Florence tried to believe those brave words. She knew there was not much to find in this desolate area. Huge tracts of land were unclaimed or abandoned. They could be going around in circles. But the three plodded on, into the teeth of the storm. Her heavy boots and the weight of her clothing made every step an effort. She could feel her breath freeze to her scarf. The wind seemed to squeeze the air out of her lungs, and a dull pain started to gnaw deep in her chest.

She knew she must go on, whatever the cost. She must keep putting one foot ahead of the other, keep stumbling next to Velma and Zindy, stay together, never lose sight of them. Oh Lord, Florence prayed, let us find something. This couldn't be the end of her hopes and dreams, of Leonard and their life together. Inside her mitten, her left thumb rubbed against the tiny diamond as if it would somehow give her strength to keep walking. She lost all sense of time and distance and direction.

With her right hand stretched ahead like a blind person feeling his way, Florence searched out every step with her booted toe, to be certain there was solid ground beneath, fearing she might plunge through the crested snow or worse yet, into the gravel pit. One step after another. Then suddenly, without warning, Florence felt something yield against her outstretched hand, something strange push against her body. In the snowy darkness, all three bumped into this resistance. Numb with cold, it took a moment to realize what it was. A fence. A wire fence!

The three held a hurried conference. A fence had to lead somewhere. But which way?

"Let's go to the right," Zindy said. "Keep walking. Hold my hand, Florence, and hang onto Velma. We're bound to find something." He pulled the reins of the protesting horses as the sleigh sank deeper into the snow. Florence took Velma's hand, knowing Zindy was just as lost as she was. She knew fences like this one enclosed acres of pastureland for the sheep; there could be no shelter for miles. But she plodded on, cheered by this faint hope, almost paralyzed from exhaustion. Fence post after fence post. Mile after mile. Oh Lord, she prayed. Help us.

At last, in the far distance, Florence saw the feeble glimmer of a light. Could it be a kerosene lamp in someone's window? It blinked through the snowflakes and her spirit lifted. They forsook the fence and with Zindy forcing the horses to follow, they pushed on toward the light. The outline of a sod hut appeared and they hurried toward it, stumbling, falling in their haste.

Zindy pounded on the door of the claim shanty and pushed it open. Delirious with joy and relief, Florence stumbled into the warmth of this heavenly place and saw an elderly man in a nightshirt peering at them, half in shock.

"What on earth are you people doing out on the night like this?" he demanded.

Zindy asked where the stable was so he could see to the horses, while Florence and Velma poured out their story. The old homesteader put on a pot of coffee while the girls stripped off their wet coats and boots, and huddled near his coal stove.

"What time is it?" Florence asked, drying her hair with a towel. It felt so delicious to be warm again.

"It's almost two o'clock in the morning!" The old timer poured a mug of coffee for each one and when Zindy came in, the four sat around the table, too overwrought to think about sleep. "It's a mercy you folks are still alive."

"Good Lord," Florence said. "Two o'clock! We've been out in that storm for nine hours."

"It's a mercy we stumbled into that fence of yours," Velma said. Her cheeks looked pinched and white, as if she might be suffering from frostbite.

The homesteader slowly looked around at the faces at his table. "When you found my fence," he said, "how did you know which way to turn? You must have lost all sense of direction."

A strange silence permeated every corner of the sod shanty as Florence felt the full weight of that question.

How indeed, did they know? She looked at Zindy. He had chosen the direction. What if he had been wrong?

"I didn't know," Zindy replied. "I just trusted to instinct. Maybe it was dumb luck, or something. By the way, what does lie in the other direction?"

The old man's eyes were as opaque as the night sky. "Nothing," he said. "Nothing at all. Just acres of unclaimed land. I ran out of fence last fall before I could get my whole place enclosed. I thought I'd wait and finish up in the spring. The few sheep I have left are safe enough in the stable. If you had gone the other way. . .well. . .you never would have made it."

Florence caught her breath. She recalled the exact moment Zindy had chosen the direction, recalled how she and Velma had followed with no other guide but blind trust.

It was a miracle they had stumbled onto this shelter just in time. Was it just dumb luck? Or had it been her constant prayer that had saved them after all.

The storm blew itself out by late morning. Zindy was able to dig his way out of the homesteader's shack, take a look at the sun and get his bearings again. He hitched up the horses and took the girls to the Maynard ranch, much to the relief of his frantic parents. The next week, the *Bowman Pioneer* headlined the story of the two teachers who were almost lost in the blizzard. It was the talk of the county for weeks afterward, and Florence sent the clipping to Leonard in her next letter.

"I promise not to go for any more long sleigh rides,"

she wrote. "This was my scariest adventure so far in North Dakota. The seminar in Bowman was a little frightening too, with all the talk about the war. Just take care of yourself and please, please, do not even think about enlisting in the army. My brother, Tom, is talking like he might do that. I think he is just sick and tired of homesteading. It's so hard to know what the future might hold."

Chapter Fifteen

The Spring of 1917

Charles Curran was an isolationist. There was no doubt about it as the political debates with the circuit riders heated up in the Curran kitchen. All during the winter and into the spring, Mr. Curran staunchly defended President Wilson's "armed neutrality." When the news leaked out about the German foreign secretary, Arthur Zimmermann, and his sneaky attempt to draw Mexico into secret alliance with the Kaiser, some of the sheep herders felt infuriated enough to go to war. But Charles Curran held firm. Then President Wilson broke diplomatic relations with Germany, another bad sign. By late spring, the outlook for peace became bleak indeed.

All this talk about war depressed Florence, but even more depressing was the strange cooling of affection from Leonard. In January and February, his letters had been ardent and loving, but then in March, the letters started to become less frequent, more formal. So many mix-ups can occur in a long distance romance. Had there been some kind of misunderstanding? With no telephone in the Curran's house, there was no way to call and have a talk. Now Florence was beginning to wonder if Leonard regretted the hasty engagement, and was just too gentlemanly to break it off. Then one fateful afternoon in April, Charles Curran came home from Rhame with some dreadful news.

"I just heard that war was declared two days ago," he said. "I saw people standing in front of the Pioneer office window, waiting for more news about it. There was a poster saying President Wilson had signed some kind of resolution on April 6th. None of us could believe it. After all his promises to keep us out of the war." Charles Curran sat down heavily on a kitchen chair, his face in his hands. "I'll never believe a politician again."

"War!" Sarah turned pale. "Does that mean our Anthony will have to go into the army? And your Leonard," she added with sympathy, turning to Florence.

"I don't know," Florence said. "I haven't heard from him for over two weeks now."

"What do you plan to do? Do you think you might postpone getting married? Will you be back here in the fall?"

Florence didn't know how to answer these questions. Mr. Saxvik had begged her to come back but she had put him off, waiting to hear something from Leonard about setting a date.

"I might come back, Sarah, if you're sure you won't mind having me as a boarder again."

"Of course we want you back," Sarah said.

"I promised Clara I'd move over to her place when the weather warmed up. I'd better go over to see her, if I can borrow the wagon."

Before she left, Florence slipped off her ring and put it in a bottom drawer of her trunk. She hadn't seen her sister all winter and now the situation with Leonard was too painful to talk about. She didn't want to be put on the spot about wedding plans. She climbed into the wagon to head for the claim shanty, to tell Clara and Robert the dreadful news about the war.

Arrangements were made to move and the next day, Florence settled into the claim shanty again. She packed away her winter coat and borrowed an old jacket of Robert's that was much too big, to wear back to school. She pinned it together with some big strong safety pins and thought it was good enough for riding horseback.

"Be sure to watch out for rattlesnakes," Robert warned when she left that Monday morning. The area was pocketed with gullies after the spring rains, and Robert advised her to stay on the road and avoid the shortcut. At first, Florence heeded the advice, although the trip along the gully saved time and was a more interesting ride.

A few days later, feeling more downcast than usual, she thought a change of scene might pick up her spirits. One of the children had said the pussy willows were in bloom along the creek bed, and she decided to take a look. Seated in the big Western saddle, she guided Buster along the gully, her gaze fixed on the water's edge, when suddenly, the horse whinnied in terror. He reared up on his hind legs and broke into a gallop. Florence felt herself being tossed into the air like a rag doll, only to be snagged upside down, with her head just inches from Buster's flying hooves and one foot still in the stirrups. The big safety pins had caught on the saddle horn, holding her prisoner. Hanging on one side of the horse, with the ground racing past her eyes, she was trapped until suddenly, Buster reared up again jarring her loose. Florence fell with a plop onto the soft wet earth while Buster pranced off a short distance. He turned to look at the fallen rider, and nonchalantly began to nibble some fresh young grass.

Florence struggled to her feet and gently called to him, "What happened? What scared you so much?"

Very slowly, she approached the horse and took hold of the reins. Then she led Buster back to the spot where he had bolted. He whinnied again in alarm. Florence looked down to the edge of the creek bed. There, on a big flat rock, squirmed a half-dozen baby rattlesnakes, sunning themselves.

Leading Buster away from the spot, she calmed him down again and re-mounted. For the remaining few weeks at the Skare shanty, Florence traveled strictly on the road.

The spring term ended in May with another box social. She had hoped to meet Mr. and Mrs. Soudnes, but they were out on another preaching mission. She had yet to lay eyes on that elusive and irresponsible couple. Florence packed up for another summer in Fargo, and returned to her job at the telephone company. She forwarded her address to Leonard although his infrequent letters had dwindled to none at all.

She couldn't help but think about him and in mid-summer, when the War Department announced a lottery plan, she felt a new stab of anxiety. The army expected to enlist three million new soldiers! All the young men would need to register for a number and the lottery drawing would start right away. Many already had volunteered and it wasn't uncommon to see a man in uniform on the city streets. The war that had seemed so distant, now felt very close to home.

Mr. Saxvik wrote several beseeching letters, pleading for her return to District 29. Having no other option, she decided to go back and this time, she moved straight to the Curran place. She found some changes at school. The two little Johnson boys had moved away. Their parents, like so many others, had given up on the rough life of homesteading. Mabel, another woebegone Soudnes child started the First Grade. Much to Florence's surprise, another newcomer turned up on the first day—Josie Peterson, age fifteen. She was a tall lanky girl with brown hair done up in braids on the top of her head, a shy expression on her face.

"I hope you don't mind if I attend school, Miss Thompson. My family has moved around so much, I never had the chance to attend very often."

"Of course you are welcome, Josie. We can figure out later what grade you should be in. We can spend some extra time together, so you can catch up with the others."

The girl's plain face brightened. "I'll do my best, Miss Thompson. I love to read. Honest I do."

Florence smiled. It always was fun to work with eager students and it felt good to be settled in a familiar place, even though she had the same old problem about lunchtime and with the Soudnes family. Sarah accepted her fate and always was sure to pack enough food. Florence went to Rhame to make peace with her mother and now that they were on speaking terms again, Isabelle invited her to come for Christmas. Florence agreed, on condition there would be no more nagging about that foolhardy trip to Minot.

In spite of Isabelle's objections, Tom enlisted in the army. He was twenty-seven and old enough to escape the draft but like many other young homesteaders, he wanted to be off on a new adventure. So Tom was absent when Florence arrived for Christmas vacation. Almost the minute she walked in the door, Isabelle made a surprising announcement.

"You will never guess what came in the mail a few days ago," Isabelle said. "To this house, of all places. It looks like a Christmas card from that man in Minot." Isabelle pulled an envelope from her apron pocket and waved it in the air.

"From Minot!" Florence grabbed the envelope and with trembling fingers, she tore it open. She hadn't heard from Leonard in six months! But inside, instead of a letter of explanation, she found only a formal Christmas card with a printed holiday greeting. Underneath was his signature. That was all.

"What do you make of it?" asked Isabelle, peering over Florence's shoulder. "I told you he is a no account man. First he can't wait to see you. Then he acts as if he hardly knows you exist."

"It's strange, I have to agree. But at least he thought of me and guessed I would be at your house for Christmas. That's something. I see his return address is still the Waverly Hotel, so he's not in the army."

Without saying another word, Florence walked to a shop in town and bought a Christmas card that was just as formal and restrained. She wrote her return address on the envelope and inside the card too, so he wouldn't make any mistake about that. She signed her name, mailed the card at the post office, and wondered what might happen next. Leonard could be so unpredictable.

Shortly after Christmas vacation, a circuit rider burst into the Curran kitchen just after suppertime. He shook the snow from his boots and pulled off his cap, a big grin on his face. It was the same rider who had loved to tease Florence about her steady stream of letters from Minot.

"Looks like you have an important message here, Miss Thompson. I thought I'd better put you first on my route."

Feeling apprehensive, Florence took the letter into the parlor to open it in privacy. She found a short note of thanks for the Christmas card and some minimal news about himself. He was still at the bank and felt more than a little worried about the slow progress of the war. But there was no explanation of his long silence.

Later that evening, Florence wrote a neutral letter of her own. She was relieved to know he was still at the bank and added that she missed him. A much warmer letter came in response and soon the letters started flying back and forth in the same pattern as the year before. The winter months flew by and spring arrived. The roads thawed out and the mud dried up. People started to be able to get around.

One April day, while Florence was walking home from school with Elvin as usual, the boy ran ahead a little bit. Then he gave out a shout of surprise and raced back to her side.

"Miss Thompson! Come and see what's in front of our house! You won't believe it. There's a big yellow roadster!"

The sight of a motorcar in Bowman County was enough to stir anyone's curiosity, and Florence gathered up her skirts to run with Elvin for a closer look. There sat a dusty-looking Buick roadster with the cloth top folded back, with wide fenders and running boards and new-style headlights that poked out in front.

"It can't be Anthony," Elvin exclaimed. "He always comes by train. Who do you think would drive clear out here in a roadster?"

Florence could think of only one person who would do something so daring and unexpected. She dashed into the kitchen to see Leonard standing there, talking with Mr. Curran. He was dressed in a long yellow duster-coat, with goggles pushed up over the brim of his yellow duster-cap. Florence felt so stunned she couldn't speak.

"I just never believed those crazy machines really worked," Mr. Curran was saying in his measured, halting way. "Those motor cars. Most people in these parts get around on horseback. But my son Anthony, in New York, writes that motorcars are all the rage in the city. How much do you figure one of these things costs?"

"About two thousand dollars," Leonard answered. "That's out of my league, I'm afraid. I rented this beauty from the Minot Garage."

Mr. Curran shook his head. "Two thousand dollars! Who could afford a price like that?"

Leonard turned to give Florence a wry smile. "I was just telling Mr. Curran here, about a wonderful future I see in automobiles. It won't be long before everyone in the whole country will own one. And not just Model T Fords but luxury cars like this one. It's the coming thing."

Florence finally found her tongue. "Leonard, why didn't you tell me you were coming?"

"It was kind of sudden. I had the chance to get away for a few days. I just got a promotion at the bank and I wanted to celebrate with you."

"You are getting up in the world, son," said Mr. Curran. "And to think you started out as a road builder.

You must be mighty proud."

Leonard took off his duster-cap. "Would you mind if Florence and I sat in the parlor for a little while. We have so much to talk about."

"You go right ahead. Sarah and Elvin are out looking at your roadster. They won't bother you. And I'm going out for a closer took, too."

Florence led the way to the parlor and tried to calm herself. This was all so bewildering—this visit, the roadster, the promotion. But Leonard always was full of surprises.

He sat beside her on the sofa, reached for her left hand and looked at her naked third finger. "Where is your ring?"

"At the bottom of my trunk. I took it off when I didn't hear from you for so long. I thought you didn't want to be engaged anymore. And now I don't know what to think. Sometimes I don't understand you at all."

"I want you to wear the ring. I want to be engaged. That's why I'm here. I want to be sure everything is all right with us."

"That's not enough for me, Leonard. What happened to us? Why didn't you write for so long? I felt. . .well, just broken-hearted. Your letters started to get so cold and formal."

"I thought *your* letters started to get cold and formal. I thought you were getting tired of waiting for me." He lifted her left hand to his lips. "I never meant to hurt you. I didn't know what to do about everything and I couldn't get away. I really thought you were tired of waiting for me."

"I wasn't tired. I don't know what you want of me."

"Florence, I want to get ahead in this world. I don't

ever want to be poor again. I need the kind of wife who will put up with my ambition. A wife who will love me for the way I am."

"Do you love me for the way I am? Will you talk with me about these things that trouble you. Will you never leave me to guess and wonder. I couldn't bear to go through a misunderstanding like this again. I need to know we are together. For always."

Leonard reached for her and they embraced in a long and tender kiss. "I'm so sorry that I hurt you. I love you. I always have—ever since the day you acted so spunky at that school program. I decided you were the one for me." He hesitated. "Now let's make up. Wear the ring. Let's be engaged again. We'll get married just as soon as I can support a wife. In the style to which she is accustomed," he added with a grin.

"That shouldn't take very long. You can see the way I live." Florence laughed, feeling as if all her worries had been dissolved and blown away. She retrieved the ring from her trunk and Leonard put it back on her finger. She felt that nothing could ever keep them apart again.

The brief visit ended all too soon. Leonard had to get back to Minot the next day and they made plans for her to visit Norma and Ed Cottington as soon as the school term ended. The circuit riders continued to deliver loving letters from Minot and Florence felt she was floating in a dream of happiness. Then one evening the rider brought a slim white envelope stamped with a different kind of postmark. The address was in Leonard's handwriting but the postmark was not from Minot. It was from Fort Snelling, the army induction center in St. Paul, Minnesota.

Dearest Florence,

I know this will upset our plans but I hope you will understand my decision. I couldn't face these people coming into the bank any longer, asking why a young man like me isn't in the Army. I don't have any real reason—except for being lucky enough to have escaped the draft. So far. However, I don't feel right about it, when so many others are enlisting and doing their part to end this terrible war. We will have to wait a little longer, my love, about getting married.

It shouldn't be very long. We should lick these Germans very soon.

I know you will be brave. You are that kind of girl. I will let you know my next address just as soon as I can. I love you very much.

Leonard

Florence felt as if the bottom had dropped out of her world. Leonard had enlisted! This dreadful war had been going on and on with no end in sight. All the peace talks had failed. Lists of casualties appeared in the city newspapers and wounded soldiers were coming home to fill up the hospitals. And still, the president said the war would be fought to its bitter conclusion, without ever saying just what that conclusion might be. Tom was in the trenches in France by now and it looked like Leonard would soon be there to join him.

Like someone caught in a nightmare, Florence taught classes by day and shed tears into her pillow at night. Nothing seemed to matter anymore—not the pitiful Soudnes children or Josie who seemed to blossom from all the personal attention, or even the Currans who always were so kind and thoughtful. May 24th marked the end of the term and Florence felt dead inside, sunk in a grim depression.

"Are you sure you won't be back next year?" asked Sarah in her gentle way. "We will miss you so much. Especially Elvin. District 29 will never get a teacher as good as you are."

"I'm not sure what I want to do. I only know I don't want to be dead broke, when Leonard comes home. I hope his training with the Machine Gun Battalion out in Washington takes a long time, and he won't have to go overseas."

"Can't you come back, Florence? Since you have to wait a while about getting married?"

"I can't make enough money teaching. I heard about a business college in Minneapolis and I have just enough for the tuition. I could start in summer school but I don't know where I could live."

"Business college? Well, if you're sure that is what you want. We have some friends in Minneapolis. The O'Connors. I could write to see if they would like to take in a nice respectable boarder like you. They probably won't charge too much, especially if you would tutor their son, Johnny. Mary O'Connor writes that he's a little slow in school. This could work out nicely, for everyone."

Florence squeezed Sarah's work-worn hand. "You have been so kind to me. I'll never forget you and Mr. Curran. Or Elvin, either. Please write to your friends. I don't know anyone in Minneapolis, and I'll need to find a boarding place."

Just then, Charles Curran appeared in the kitchen doorway. "I'd like to add some parting thoughts, Florence.

It has been a pleasure to have you in our home. You are a good person, the kind of person who knows when to talk. And when to keep silent."

"That's one of the nicest compliments I've ever received," Florence said. "I'll always remember that."

"Elvin has loved having you as his teacher," Sarah said, dabbing at her eyes. "I doubt any new teacher would buy a Christmas tree for the children, out of her own money."

That was high praise indeed. Scrupulous Sarah knew better than anyone, the value of a dollar. Florence blinked back a tear. She had stayed with the Currans longer than any other boarding family. Two years. It was terribly hard to say goodbye.

Florence went through another tearful farewell with Clara and Robert, all of them knowing it might be years before they would meet again. She went to Rhame for a last goodbye to the family, and to break the news about going to business school. For once, Isabelle seemed pleased with her decision.

"It's about time one of my children should amount to something," Isabelle said. "None of them have. So far. All poor as church mice. Be sure to write to Tom before he gets himself killed in France."

With Isabelle's gloomy prediction ringing in her ears, Florence boarded the train for the long tiresome ride to Minneapolis. There would be no school bell to ring again in the fall. Or that's what Florence thought on that sad day in the beginning of June, 1918.

Chapter Sixteen

Minneapolis and the Armistice

After arriving at the station, Florence boarded the trolley in Minneapolis. Using the directions Mrs. O'Connor had sent, she got off at the proper stop and found the tall brick, two-story house on Patterson Street. It sat on a city block of houses that looked essentially the same, all in a row like a close-drill soldiers, with narrow green lawns that fronted a paved street. Tall leafy trees lined the sidewalks and arched overhead, lending an atmosphere of restrained gentility.

Sarah Curran had told her about this Irish Catholic family; how they had just recently lost their eldest son, George, to the influenza epidemic. The daughter, Monica Anne, was bright and precocious, while Johnny was the boy who needed a tutor. The family didn't want to believe he was retarded.

Florence never had known any Catholics, Irish or otherwise, but according to Pastor Lundberg, the stern Lutheran minister who had conducted her confirmation class, Catholics worshipped statues in their churches and never read the Bible. They made a particular fuss over the Virgin Mary and believed in a place called Purgatory. Florence felt a bit leery about being exposed to such odd beliefs, but she gathered up her courage and pushed the pearly white doorbell. She heard a loud shrill ring and the bright, round face of a girl about twelve, peeked out the elaborate, frosty-windowed front door.

"You must be the boarder," she said. "Come in. I'm Monica Anne."

"Hello. I'm Miss Thompson."

"Mama, the boarder is here!" shrieked Monica Anne, who raced up the wide, carpeted staircase, leaving Florence in the vestibule. She noticed a pale boyish face peeking around the parlor door.

"Hello," she said. "You must be Johnny."

The face disappeared. Monica came bounding down the stairs, her raven-colored braids flying behind her. She wore a low-waisted dress with a sash tied at the hips, with long white stockings and shiny black patent-leather slippers.

"Mama is still at church," Monica announced. "I thought she would be home by now, but she's still saying prayers for George. He's dead, you know. You're going to have George's room but you'd better not touch anything in it or Mama will have a fit."

"I'll try not to touch anything, Monica Anne." Florence followed the girl up the stairs, feeling more and more out of place in this elegant house. There were sconces of electric light bulbs on the wood paneled walls, and Oriental rugs on the polished wood floors. The broad staircase landing had been converted into a sort of shrine where a figure of an almost naked Jesus hung on display. Below the figure was a low table with little round candles burning. Next to the crucifix hung a portrait of the Virgin Mary with a blue mantle covering her head. At least

Florence thought this must be the Virgin Mary. Pictures like that did not appear in the Lutheran catechism.

"Don't you have any more luggage than that?" asked Monica Anne as they reached the top of the staircase, eyeing Florence's shabby green valise.

"I shipped my trunk on the train. It should come in a day or two." Florence followed the girl into a masculine room just off the upstairs hall. There was a narrow single bed covered with a worsted spread and on one wall, Florence saw a tall bookshelf crammed with adventure novels. Next to that stood a heavy mahogany desk and a rusted metal anchor that looked as if it had been rescued from an ancient ship. "How old was George?" asked Florence, surveying the pictures of sailboats and schooners.

"Twenty-two. He had wanted to join the navy but my mother wouldn't let him. Then he got sick and died. You must be almost the same age as George. My mother said you used to be a schoolteacher. I hope we can have some fun together. It's so tiresome around here with Mama in church all the time, saying prayers for George."

Florence never had heard of saying prayers for the dead. Pastor Lundberg said people went straight to heaven or hell, and God didn't need any instructions about that.

"I hope we can be good friends," Florence said. "I'd like to unpack now. Will you let me know when your mother gets home?"

Monica ignored the hint. She perched on the bed to watch while Florence unpacked her valise, and kept up a steady stream of questions about what sort of children went to a country school, and how did a teacher manage all the grades at the same time. During this one-sided conversation, a light tap-tap sounded at the bedroom door. A slender woman with jet-black hair came in. She looked about forty-five and wore a severe black dress that made her pale face appear even more pallid. Her eyes were red rimmed from crying.

"Hello. I'm Mary O'Connor. I'm so glad you found the place all right. I know you're not used to the city. It must have been terrible, to live way out in a wilderness like North Dakota." She turned to her daughter. "Now Monica Anne, I don't want you pestering Miss Thompson with a lot of questions. You run along now." Monica rolled her eyes and disappeared into the hall.

"Sarah Curran tells me you are a very good teacher," Mary O'Connor continued. "And you might be interested in tutoring our Johnny."

"I'm going to be very busy. I'll have my own studying to do at the business college."

"Well, I just wonder, now. About the tutoring. Johnny is falling behind in his school work and I'm so worried about him."

"I'll try to help if I can. Ask Johnny to bring his books to my room after supper. We'll see what we can do." Florence didn't ask about payment for her time, and Mrs. O'Connor didn't offer.

"Thank you, Miss Thompson. After the loss of our dear George, I just couldn't concentrate on anything. It would mean so much to me, if you could help Johnny this summer."

"How long ago did that happen? About George."

"It's been four months now. I don't think I'll ever get over it." Mrs. O'Connor's glance darted to the desk. "You won't move that anchor, will you? Or touch the books. I want to keep the room exactly the way George left it." She took out a handkerchief and dabbed at her eyes. "We'll have dinner at six o'clock. When Mr. O'Connor gets home from the office. He has a very important position with the electric company and he likes to eat right on time." Her glance swept around the room in a final survey, as if memorizing every detail, and closed the door.

That evening, Florence was introduced to Mr. O'Connor. He was a tall, barrel-chested man with dark bushy eyebrows, slicked back hair, and wore a conservative business suit with a starched collar.

"Oh, oh, don't sit there, Miss Thompson," he said when Florence pulled out a chair at the dinner table. "That chair is reserved for George. We like to feel he is still with us."

Florence moved over to a chair next to Monica Anne. Mary O'Connor put a big platter of corned beef and steamed cabbage on the table. This was a curious dish Florence never had seen before, with round black pellets sprinkled over it.

"Not enough peppercorns," Mr. O'Connor announced from his place at the head of the table. "What do you think, Miss Thompson?"

"There is quite enough pepper," Mary O'Connor snapped, before Florence could answer.

While the two continued their duel about seasoning and how the beef should have been cooked, Florence turned her attention to the ten-year-old boy seated across from her. There was a dull look on his face and he picked at the peppercorns with his fork and pushed them under his plate.

"What grade are you in, Johnny?" Florence asked.

"He's still in the Third," Monica replied. "For the second time."

"That's enough out of you, Monica Anne," Mr. O'Connor interrupted. "Miss Thompson is going to tutor him and he'll catch up in no time." The girl gave a dubious look to Florence and picked all the peppercorns off her meat. Florence took a small bite of the corned beef, her first taste of Irish cooking. She thought it was very delicious but she could understand why the children didn't like the peppercorns. They were much too hot to eat.

Later, Johnny brought his schoolbooks to Florence's room, ready for his first lesson. He slumped into the chair next to the desk and stared at her morosely.

"Let's start with spelling," Florence said, picking up a book that looked brand new, as if it never had been opened. "What words did you learn today?" School was still in session in Minneapolis.

"I dunno," Johnny said. He picked at a piece of lint on his corduroy knickers and brushed back a lock of his dark hair. He was a nice-looking boy but there was no mistaking his lack of interest.

"Well, let's look at your arithmetic book. What problems did you work on today?"

"I dunno," Johnny relied.

"Don't you like school at all?"

"I dunno. Not much, I guess."

It didn't take long to realize that Johnny was not going to learn anything. He simply could not concentrate and there was nothing she could do about that. These evening sessions would be a total waste of time, but Florence didn't want to tell his mother the truth. Mary O'Connor seemed distressed enough, without adding to her burdens.

"Well, Johnny, that's enough for tonight. Please study this list of spelling words, and we'll try again tomorrow."

The next day, Florence took the trolley downtown to Nicolet Avenue, and an austere-looking brick office building with the top floor reserved for the business college. After she paid the tuition and bought the required books on shorthand and typing, she peeked into one of the classrooms. It contained rows of wooden tables with shiny black typewriters on each one, all with blank keys. A big display keyboard was in the front of the room, hanging like a pull-down map, so the students could fix their attention on that and not on their fingers. The keyboard looked so complicated, with the letters of the alphabet in such peculiar places, Florence wondered if she could ever memorize it.

In the afternoon, back in her room, Florence paged through the shorthand book and felt even more disheartened, looking at all those squiggles and symbols. Could she really learn all this in just a six-month course? She began to wonder if business school had been such a good idea.

That evening, seated next to the ghost of George at the dinner table, she listened to Mr. and Mrs. O'Connor argue over the discouraging progress of the war, what was wrong with General Pershing's strategy, and how much bay leaf should have been used in the beef stew. Johnny came to her room that evening, unable to spell a single word from the previous lesson.

After he left, Florence went downstairs to find the newspaper Mr. O'Connor had tossed on the floor near his easy chair. The headlines told about reports of poison gas being used in the trenches and all manner of other atrocities the Germans employed. Now that she had access to a daily newspaper, Florence felt even more fearful about Leonard. He was still in training, learning how to take apart and use a machine gun. In a way, he was fortunate. Tom's outfit hardly had any training at all, before he was shipped to France.

The days were filled with shorthand and typing classes. In the evenings, she listened to Mr. O'Connor find fault with everything put on the table. Florence liked the Irish stew and the kidney pie and all these new recipes, but she longed for a cup of good Norwegian coffee. In this household, only strong black tea was served for breakfast and dinner, a peculiar brand that left a bitter after-taste even if sweetened with a cube of sugar.

Monica Anne continued to bounce into her room unannounced, with questions and comments far beyond her years. Monica Anne could converse on any topic from the wrong-headed tactics of trench warfare to the probability of life after death. She wondered endlessly if it was worthwhile for her mother to spend hours every day in church, praying George's way out of purgatory. Florence wondered how one child in a family could be so bright, while the other couldn't do a simple problem in arithmetic.

All that summer of 1918, influenza haunted the streets of Minneapolis. The newspapers had pages of obituaries and every slight infection was a signal for deep concern. When Florence came home from class one day to find her landlady sick in bed, she felt very alarmed. "Can I get you something?" she asked.

"It's just a headache, Miss Thompson." Mary O'Connor raised her head from the double bed in the many-windowed master bedroom. "I know influenza symptoms all too well. Just think of what I went through with our dear George. But I would like a cup of tea, if you don't mind."

Down in the kitchen, Florence lit a burner on the gas stove and put the teakettle on to boil. Mr. O'Connor wasn't satisfied as yet with the stoves made by the electric company. She admired this improvement over the coal stove that belonged to Mrs. Curran and this modern way to cook by just lighting a pilot flame. She read the directions on the box and measured a teaspoonful of tealeaves, put them in a china pot and poured in the hot water. Just then, Mr. O'Connor came home early from the office. He walked into the kitchen and lifted the lid on the teapot.

"What are you doing, Miss Thompson? Do you call that sickly mixture—tea? That's no way to do it. Here, let me show you."

He seized a two-quart saucepan from the cupboard, half filled it with cold water and shook in some tealeaves. He placed the pan on the gas burner, turned up the flame and started stirring until the mixture looked dark as beef bouillon.

"Do you boil the tea on the stove?" Florence felt stunned. She had little experience in the kitchen but she always had thought tea was supposed to be steeped in a china pot.

When Mr. O'Connor thought the tea had boiled long enough, he poured a cup and Florence took it upstairs to Mrs. O'Connor. "Are you feeling better?"

Mary O'Connor sat up in bed and took a tentative sip. "This is delicious. Why, I couldn't have done better myself. And you tell me you don't know much about cooking!"

"Mr. O'Connor made it. I'll ask him to help me with supper tonight. Now you just rest and get well."

Under Mr. O'Connor's critical eye, Florence warmed up some chicken soup left over from the day before, and added some seasonings according to his instructions. She toasted bread in the oven to his satisfaction and hoped to never need to set foot in the O'Connor kitchen again. Mary O'Connor was good as new the next day.

Two weeks later, Florence awoke with a fever. Her body ached and she couldn't lift her head from the pillow. Her landlady came to check on Florence and placed a hand on the patient's burning forehead.

"I know these symptoms all too well," Mary O'Connor said grimly. "It's influenza and there's no use calling a doctor. None of them would come anyway, and take the chance of getting exposed. All you can do is stay in bed and drink lots of fluids. I'll ask Monica Anne to bring you a cup of tea."

Day after day, Florence's temperature hovered at 103 degrees. Monica Anne peeked into her room at all hours, keeping a careful distance. Mary O'Connor brought cups of bitter tea and the doctor came in spite of the fear of contagion. An entire week passed and Mary O'Connor resigned herself to the patient's early demise. "The doctor said there is no hope. The only thing to do is send for a priest."

"Oh, no. I don't want to see a priest. I feel better today."

Mary shook her head. "The patient always feels better

just before the end. We don't have time to waste. I'll send for Father Ryan."

"If you must send for someone, please call Pastor Blomquist." Florence had started attending the Lutheran church in the neighborhood, and knew the pastor slightly.

Mary stood firm. "I'm going to call Father Ryan. We don't want to take any chances."

"But I'm a Lutheran," Florence protested.

A short time later, Mary O'Connor returned with a pale young priest in tow, dressed in the traditional black clergy suit with a Roman collar, and carrying a small black bag with equipment for the Last Rites. He sat on a chair as far from Florence's bed as possible and Mary brought a tray with a pot of tea. Gamely, the priest tried to drink a cup, while Mary offered a floodgate of information about George and his symptoms and Florence and her symptoms. Exactly the same.

"It was kind of you to come," Florence whispered. "But I'm a Lutheran. I want to see my own pastor."

The young priest put down his teacup and shot a dark look at Mary O'Connor. He mumbled his apologies and hurried from the sick room. Now Mary decided it was time to call on a Higher Authority.

"Florence, there isn't much time left. Now drink this cup of tea and pray as hard as you can to the Virgin Mary."

"What?" Florence groaned. She believed if she could just stop this parade of visitors and get some sleep, she might be able to pull through.

"I'll light a candle," Mary continued. "You might not believe in the Virgin but you pray, anyway."

"I pray to God. I have prayed. And prayed. Now please, let me get some sleep."

Mary looked at her sharply. "But you didn't pray to the Virgin Mary, now did you? If you would . . .I think you might be all right. Please, Florence. I know what happens to people when they get influenza. I'll wait outside the door," she persisted. "I'll peek in when you are finished with your prayer."

Florence saw the door close and she felt herself sinking into inky blackness, worried that she was becoming delirious. If she could only sleep. . .keep Mary O'Connor and all these people out of her room. In a few more minutes, the bedroom door opened again.

"Did you pray to the Virgin?"

"Yes, I did," she lied. "Now please let me rest. Go light some more candles and I don't want any more tea." She heard Mary quietly slip out of the room and Florence fell into a deep sound sleep.

Slowly, slowly, in spite of all the ministrations and the unwanted visits, Florence began to re-gain her strength. She was able to read several letters that had come from Leonard. She sorted them out by the dates on the postmarks and relished each one. His loving words made her feel so much better, until she opened the most recent letter. Leonard's battalion was due to go overseas. Exactly when, he didn't know.

October faded into November. Florence felt strong enough to go to the business college to ask about a partial refund on her tuition. The answer was a definite no. After catching up on the room rent, Florence's small store of cash had dwindled close to zero.

One gloomy day, to get her mind off her worries, she took the trolley downtown to go window-shopping. Now Leonard was at his Port of Embarkation and due to board a troop ship any day. She couldn't bear to think about it, or even ponder what might happen next.

Strolling along Nicolet Avenue, she stopped in front of Donaldson's Department Store, to admire the new fashions on the manikins in the window. It didn't cost anything to merely look. She was absorbed in this when slowly, without being aware of it at first, she noticed a strange excitement in the air. She heard automobile horns honking . . . trolley bells clanging. . .people shouting. Strangers on the sidewalk began to joyfully hug one another. Florence grabbed the arm of a passerby. "What is it? What's going on?"

"Why, lady! Don't you know?" he answered, looking jubilant. "The war is over! The news was just posted in the Tribune window. The Armistice has been signed! The Kaiser has surrendered and the war is over!"

The Armistice! Florence hadn't seen a newspaper for days. She had been too sick to read about the negotiations leading up to this glorious day. And now. . .now the promise of peace in the world finally had come true.

The heavy burden lifted. Her prayers had been answered. Leonard had been saved from going overseas and they could get married at last.

A little later, back in her room, she wrote a long letter to Leonard, expressing her joy and telling him the news of her complete recovery from the dreaded influenza. She knew it might be several months before he would be mustered out of the army, so what should she do in the meantime? She paused, pen in hand, mulling over some ideas. She didn't want him to find her defeated and impoverished, back home with her mother. No. She had to find a job right away and the next school term would begin in early December. There still was a chance to find an opening. Somewhere.

As soon as she finished the letter, she wrote another to Tillie Thomason back in Swift County. Perhaps Tillie could come up with a miracle.

By return mail, a letter arrived from the superintendent. There was no school available in Swift County but over in Lincoln County, there was a school near Hendricks, Minnesota, a school that needed a teacher desperately. The current one had been fired for misconduct. This would be a difficult school, Tillie warned. There were sixty-five pupils enrolled, more than any two teachers could decently handle.

Tillie went on to say the boarding place was with the John Waugh family. The house was very crowded with five children and no private room for the teacher. The place was anything but desirable, but the address of the Waugh farm was enclosed, just in case Florence should want the job.

It didn't take long to make up her mind. Florence wrote to say she would be very pleased to accept the position.

Chapter Seventeen
The Hendricks School

On the first day of the winter term, along with the troop of Waugh children, Florence trudged the mile and a half to school through deep snow. She unlocked the door of the schoolhouse, shook the snow from her boots, and stepped into the cloakroom. Then she stopped in her tracks, to stare in complete disbelief. Scrawled on the walls of the cloakroom with crayon, ink, pencil, in a rainbow of colors, was every filthy word Florence ever had heard, and some she never had known before. There were childish scrawly drawings of private body parts that made Florence blush. Never, in all her years of teaching, had she seen anything remotely like this.

Currie Waugh giggled and poked his brother, Raymond, in the ribs. The three Waugh girls giggled too. Then Irene, the eldest, spoke up. "If you think that looks bad, Miss Thompson, you should see the privies."

"I guess you'd better show me." Picking up her skirts, Florence headed over to the girls' outhouse with Irene leading the way. Everywhere the eye could see in the dim light, on the wood plank seat and the studded walls, were more of the same obscene words and drawings. The two marched over to the boys' privy. Same thing, only worse.

"We'd better go in the schoolhouse and light the stove," Florence said with a sigh. How could children think of such things? Where had they heard such words? These children must be monsters and the school board must be deaf, dumb and blind, to allow such filth.

Inside the classroom, she found the walls were clean and the place looked more normal. After the room warmed up, while the Waugh children hovered around the coal stove, she started to put the lessons for the day on the blackboard. She had to think of something tactful to say to these children, something that would get them on her side about cleaning up this mess as quickly as possible. Why hadn't those terrible walls been painted over? Then she came up with the usual answer. Lack of money.

When it was time for classes to begin, she went outdoors to ring the school bell and found the huge crowd she expected. Sixty-five children. They filed in, the older ones herding the younger brothers and sisters. She knew this district was populated with large families, according to what Mrs. Waugh had told her the night before. Ten or even twelve children were not unusual for families in this district. They took their seats with a minimum of confusion and Florence rang the school bell again.

"Good morning. I'm Miss Thompson. Your new teacher." She looked at the sea of upturned faces. How could she remember all these names?

"I have been looking around here," she continued, "and I think some children long, *long ago,* must have written the terrible things in the cloakroom and the privies. I feel very sure it could not have been *you* children, attending here today. I see that all of you look much too fine and intelligent, to have written such ugly, vulgar words."

Florence paused. A few of the older boys smirked and grinned at one another. Most of the others sat bolt upright, looking very serious. "Do we all agree that we don't want to see our schoolhouse looking like this?" Sixty-five heads nodded in affirmation.

"Good," she continued. "I have an idea how to change things for the better. How many of you have left-over wallpaper at home?" This was a reasonable question, since almost every farmhouse had a parlor decorated with vivid floral wallpaper. Almost all the hands shot up.

"Splendid. If you don't have wallpaper, you could bring picture pages from Sears and Roebuck catalogues. We can make some paste with flour and water and wallpaper the cloakroom and the outhouses. What do you think of that? How many would like to help with this project?" She paused again, waiting for their approval. "I must warn you, we will do this job *after* class. So that means staying after school for a few days."

An enthusiastic murmur rose from the pupils. Florence knew it would be more fun for the children to cut and paste, rather than try to scrub the walls clean. That would be exhausting and they might lose interest.

"Good. Thank you for your help. Now we will begin with the opening exercises. I want the younger children to sit up here in front. How many are beginning readers?"

Fifteen primary grade children raised their hands. Florence felt overwhelmed. She could spend an entire day with this group alone. *Three* teachers couldn't do justice with this school. She went through the opening exercises, made the assignments for the older children, and then attempted to learn the names of her beginners. There were so many! The entire morning seemed a blur of trying to be everywhere at once.

Lunchtime came as a welcome relief. After downing the contents of their lunch pails while seated at their desks, the children went out to play. All but one. Thirteen-year-old Irene Waugh hovered near the cloakroom door, watching her. Irene was not only her student but her bedmate as well. The jam-packed Waugh house had only one room designated for the girls with two double beds. One was for little Perle and Eva. The other for the teacher and this bony girl who seemed all elbows and knees.

"Did you want to say something, Irene?" Florence asked.

"I have an idea, Miss Thompson," the girl replied, moving closer to the desk. "I want to help you. I used to help Miss Gruenwald in the fall term, and teach the beginning readers. I know all about phonics cards and the whole system."

"That's a fine idea. I certainly could use some help. But you will have to keep up all your own work with the Eighth Grade."

"Oh, pshaw, Miss Thompson. That's such easy stuff. I could teach all the primary grades, if you'd let me. I get so bored reading history and civics all the time. I'm ready for English literature. I like to read plays."

"Let me think about this, Irene. We can talk more about it after school. Now you go out and play with the others."

The afternoon was dreadful. The beginning readers were restless while Florence was busy with the times tables in arithmetic for the older students. The little ones disturbed the middle students who were trying to read the history assignment. The only way she could calm everyone down was to hold a story hour, a treat she usually saved for Friday afternoons. By three o'clock, Florence had a splitting headache and dismissed classes early. Irene stayed to erase the blackboard and watch Florence write out the lessons for the next day.

"Well, Miss Thompson. How about letting me take the beginning readers tomorrow? This was a mess, today. I don't want you to just up and quit, the way the last teacher did."

"I heard she got fired."

"Miss Gruenwald got so upset one day, she lost her temper and slapped a couple of the boys. I think she wanted to quit, anyway. She was such a grouch. Not like you at all. Please let me help you, Miss Thompson. I'm very grown up for my age. I was out sick for a whole year. That's why I'm still in the Eighth Grade."

"All right, Irene. You can take charge of the beginning readers. But remember, you have to keep up your studies. I'm not going to let you just slide by."

"Don't worry about that. I want to go to high school and I'll have to pass the exams to get in."

The two walked home together and the mile and a half seemed an eternity. Irene pelted her with more questions than Monica Anne O'Connor. Irene wanted to know every detail of Florence's private life, and all about the diamond ring she wore and how soon she planned to get married. Irene begged for a look inside Florence's precious trunk. "I want to see all your dresses," she declared. "Every one."

"I'll show you someday. But right now, I'm too tired. I'd like to take a nap when we get home. Could I have our room to myself, for a little while?" They arrived at the Waugh kitchen door.

"Ugh! I smell saurkraut!" Irene wrinkled her nose. "When I have a home of my own, I'll never cook saurkraut. I hate it."

Florence went in and hung up her coat. She never had tasted saurkraut and had to agree there was a very strong odor. "Hello, Mrs. Waugh. I hope you've had a better day than I've had."

"Now, Florence. Please call me Hulda. We go by first names here. I hope Irene hasn't worn you out completely, with all her questions. She nearly drove the last teacher crazy."

Hulda Waugh stuffed some corncobs into her black iron stove and turned to smile at Florence. She was small-boned and thin and wore a simple housedress. She was a soul of patience with her rambunctious children, and frugal as a German housewife. Since there was no bedroom in the house for the boys, Hulda had created one for them in a corner of the kitchen. There was a couch that made into a double bed, a place where Currie and Raymond could scuffle with each other, when they weren't teasing their sisters.

The Waugh house was a dwelling that had grown like Topsy in *Uncle Tom's Cabin*, with a room added here and there as the need arose, without any sort of plan. Closets were minimal and hallways non-existent. Florence had to walk through Hulda and John's room, to reach the crowded bedroom she shared with the girls. The only room with any charm was the big dining room, with a broad window that overlooked the apple orchard. The little parlor usually was too cold for use in the winter.

Florence retreated to the bedroom with Irene following like a shadow. Irene plopped herself on the bed, to watch Florence change into a housedress. "You have such beautiful clothes," she sighed. "Won't you please let me look in your trunk?"

"Not now. You mustn't ever touch anything in my trunk. This is all the privacy I have and you must learn to respect the property of others."

The girl looked at the trunk with longing eyes and it was obvious the temptation would be too strong to resist. Florence hunted for the key to the trunk and slipped it on a chain to wear around her neck. "This is just insurance, Irene. I don't want you to get into into my trunk. Not ever."

At supper that evening, Florence sat next to John Waugh. He was a quiet man, just as thin and wiry as his wife, a hard-working farmer who barely managed to scratch out a living. Florence couldn't help but wonder how these two simple, down-to-earth people, ever had spawned a child as precocious as their eldest daughter.

The next day, Irene took charge of the beginners and a semblance of peace settled over the classroom. Work began on the wallpaper project. The children loved to cut and paste and within days, the hideous walls in the cloakroom and privies were transformed into a crazy quilt of flowery patterns. Florence started to depend upon Irene, who was like a teacher's aide. There were days when Florence wished she could have two more just like her. But there were nights in the crowded bedroom, when she wished the saucy, impudent girl would vanish in a puff of smoke.

With Christmas coming up so soon, Irene offered to write a skit for the program, and to supervise the carol singing. She helped with the decorations and showed the little ones how to hold their scissors to cut the construc-

Florence and John Waugh — Waugh Farm 1919

tion paper. On the last day before the program, Florence and her star student stayed late at school, to put some finishing touches on the tree. By then, it was getting close to dark and the Christmas Angel needed to be put in place.

"Doesn't the tree look beautiful?" Florence said, stepping back to admire the strings of cranberries and popcorn and the paper chains. "Do you mind if I borrow your sweater, Irene? It's getting chilly in here and I don't want to put any more coal in the stove. We're almost ready to leave. You'd better dump the water out of the pail, so it doesn't freeze."

Irene handed her the sweater, a cardigan Hulda had knit with imitation pearl buttons in front, and dutifully disposed of the water. Standing on a chair, Florence reached up to adjust the angel that looked like a tiny rag doll dressed in pink. A kerosene lamp hung from a wall bracket near the tree, and Florence decided some light would enhance the total effect. Reaching into her pocket, she found a matchbox and then lifted the glass chimney. As she reached over to light the wick, the lamp exploded with a resounding pop, shooting flames in every direction.

"Oh, my God! The tree is on fire!" Florence screamed. She ripped off the sweater and used it to smother the flames, pressing each branch into the folds of the garment. By the time the fire was out, Irene's sweater looked like an ashen rag and the tree was ruined. "Oh dear. Look what's happened. I'm so sorry, Irene. I'll buy you a new sweater."

"Why do you make such a fuss about an old sweater when the whole schoolhouse could have burned down. You're a hero, Miss Thompson. You saved this place. But what will we do about the tree?"

The few branches that remained hung in limp disarray. Christmas Angel had gone up in smoke. The entire room was filled with an acrid odor. Florence got down from her perch and slumped into her teacher's chair.

"All's well that ends well, I guess. Only there isn't

time to get a new tree and decorate it too. The program is tomorrow night."

Irene swept up the debris of popcorn and cranberries, still muttering about how silly the teacher was to worry about a sweater when the schoolhouse could have burned down. When they got home, Florence called the chairman of the school board and he advised her to go ahead with the program, without a tree.

Irene was in her element the next evening, as star and producer of the skit. The program was a big success and afterward, the parents clustered around Florence to thank her for saving the schoolhouse.

"Why do you feel so bad about the sweater?" Hulda asked, helping to clean up the last of the Christmas celebration. "I say it is cheaper to knit another sweater, than to build a new schoolhouse." Hulda, as always, was a very practical person.

Florence spent the holiday with Grandmother Betsy and savored every moment of luxurious privacy, with no little girls to share her room and no Irene to ask dozens of questions. It was very hard to go back to the crowded Waugh farm and harder still, to keep waiting and waiting for Leonard. It was taking months to go through the process of getting mustered out of the army.

January was bitter cold with the temperature dipping way below zero. Diseases of every kind ravaged the district—measels, mumps, diphtheria and pneumonia. It was a rare day when Florence had full attendance. No matter how she coaxed the coal store for a little more heat, the schoolhouse stayed frigid. Sometimes the mittens didn't thaw out for the entire day. Irene cooked soup on the schoolhouse stove, so the children would have something hot for lunch. Florence conducted exercise breaks to warm up the chilled fingers and toes. On some days, it was simply too cold to expect the children to go to school at all.

One icy February day, Florence stayed late to cut out Valentines, and insisted that Irene should go home with the others. The constant commotion at both boarding place and school, was getting to be more than she could bear. Florence took her time laying out the red construction paper and stirring up paste to get ready for the next day. Then she picked her way home in the dark by lantern light. When she pushed open the bedroom door, feeling exhausted from her long day, she found Irene sitting on their bed, happily dabbing some of Florence's treasured rice powder on her nose.

"Irene! How dare you get into my things!" Florence's hand flew to her neck. The key was still there, hanging on its chain. The little imp must have picked the lock. "Irene, you must apologize this minute. Don't you dare get into my trunk again."

Irene burst into tears. "You never showed me your things the way you promised. I kept asking and asking."

"There isn't space in this room to unpack anything. Besides, my property is my business." It was hard to stay angry with Irene. She looked so funny sitting there, caught red-handed, with rice powder scattered on the bedspread.

"I hate this life on the farm," Irene sobbed. "I can hardly wait to go off to high school and live in town and start living my own life. Do you know what I want to be when I grow up? A famous actress. Someday, you'll be glad you knew me, I'll be so famous. And I will wear face powder and rouge and lipstick. So there."

Florence laughed. "Irene, you have so much talent, I'm sure you will be a success at whatever you decide to do."

"You can laugh now. But just wait. I'll be famous, I promise you. I'm going to be on the stage."

"Perhaps you will. But if I ever catch you in my trunk again, I will tell your father. And you will get a whipping."

Finally, in late February, Leonard was released from his battalion. He was mustered out in St. Paul and on a Saturday morning, he rented a car and drove straight to the Waugh farm. This was a visit that sent Irene into an ecstasy of excitement. From the moment Leonard walked in the door, wearing his civilian clothes, she bombarded him with questions, and all during the special lunch Hulda had prepared.

"You can see why I'm nearly going crazy here," Florence said later, when they were able to grab a few minutes alone in the chilly parlor.

"You can bet I do. That girl doesn't ever let up, does she?" He hesitated, as if reluctant to bring up the subject foremost in their minds. "Florence, you know I'd marry you this minute, if I could. But I'm afraid that is out of the question. A soldier's pay isn't very much and I have to save some money first. The president of the bank in Minot has promised to give me my old job back. This will be like starting all over again."

Florence sighed. "I understand. I couldn't leave here

until the end of the term anyway, much as I'd love to pack up and go with you right this minute." She gave him a reassuring kiss and they made plans for another visit to the Cottingtons in June. Now that the war had ended, all the people in the country were picking up the pieces of their lives. They would just have to do the same.

Winter melted into spring. Letters flew back and forth. Now Leonard was settled at the Waverly Hotel and busy adding to his bank account, while Florence was barely able to survive from one paycheck to the next. Then one evening at supper, John Waugh made a startling comment, one that was totally unexpected.

"Have you heard, Florence, there's a strange story going around about you. That you are a divorcee. I don't know what to make of it."

"A divorcee! How silly. Who told you such a thing?"

"Henry Bierson. You know how Henry likes to talk."

Henry Bierson often visited at the farm and he had a reputation as a terrible gossip. Florence felt shocked. Being a divorced woman was the next thing to being a fallen woman, and such talk could spell her ruination. She felt determined to discover the source of this ugly rumor and the next time Henry Bierson came over to chew the fat with John, she questioned him.

"I did hear tell about you being a divorcee," Henry admitted, wiping his hand on his overalls. "I heard it from Mr. Lundstrom and he should know. He's a teacher too."

Mr. Lundstrom was the only male teacher in the district and Florence hardly knew him. "I'm going over to see that man right away, and put a stop to this stupid story."

She asked directions for the teacher's boarding place and borrowed the buggy from John. A little later, she whirled into the designated farmyard, seething with right-eous indignation. She confronted Mr.Lundstrom, a tall, unassuming man who looked very puzzled.

"You have started a vicious rumor about me, sir. And I want to get to the bottom of it. How could you tell Henry Bierson, the worst gossip in six counties, that I am a divorcee? The truth is I never have been married. I don't know what you have against me. I don't even know you."

Lundstrom scratched his head. "You think I said something like that? Now if that doesn't beat all. But I think I know what this is all about."

"Then tell me." Florence could hardly control her impatience. Lundstrom had to be the slowest-thinking man in the world.

"When we heard a new teacher was coming to the Hendricks school, after that last one got fired, well, I got to talking with Henry Bierson. He said a Miss Thompson was coming on a sort of a last-minute call. And I said how do we know she is a Miss Thompson. She could be a Mrs. Thompson, for all we know. It was a foolish thing to say. But I never thought it would start up all this commotion."

"Foolish is right. You should know better. You know how gossip flies around. You know how people can jump to all the wrong conclusions, and think a Mrs. teaching school would have to be a divorcee. You know that married women can't teach."

"I hope you can forgive me, Miss Thompson. I didn't mean any harm."

"All right. I will forgive you but on one condition. You will tell everyone you see that you were wrong, and that you are sorry you said such a thing. I am not a divorcee."

Still feeling furious, Florence went off in a flurry of

hoof beats. Sometimes it was so tiresome to be a woman. Men didn't have to defend their virtue all the time. Men could marry and not lose their teaching jobs. Life was so unfair. If she could keep on teaching after she married Leonard, they could make ends meet. But instead, they had to wait and wait, just because of all these stupid rules and regulations. And it looked like nothing would change, until women could finally get the vote.*

John Waugh had a little venture on the side, other than farming. He was the only beekeeper in Lincoln County and Hulda kept a list of customers for honey. It was a thriving little business. From her bedroom window, Florence could watch the activity around the wooden hives set up on stilts in the apple orchard. John kept a careful watch on the bees, lest a colony should suddenly decide to migrate to a hollow tree in some distant field. A colony often did, if the hives should become too crowded. He enjoyed pottering around with the bees and Hulda enjoyed the added income.

Accustomed as she was to living in old houses, Florence hardly noticed the creaks and groans that came from the floors and woodwork. She didn't pay much attention when the wall in the dining room started to show some tiny web-like wrinkles. But when one little crack in the center of the wall slowly turned into a bigger crack, even the children started to notice.

---

*After decades of struggle, women finally got the right to vote in 1920.

"Now what do you think is happening to this old house," Hulda asked one evening, as she placed a gooseberry pie on the table. "The floors creak and the doors are lop-sided, and now I think I hear odd noises coming from that crack in the wall."

Irene looked up from her plate. "What kind of noises, Ma. Maybe the house is haunted."

"What nonsense, child. You read too many books. I hear a buzzing sound so it can't be a colony of ants. It's a buzzing maybe like. . ."

"Like bees," Florence finished. The words were hardly out of her mouth, when the crack in the wall split open with a loud crash. Honey oozed over the faded wallpaper and down to the wood floor.

"Sakes alive!" cried Hulda. "Just look at this mess."

Florence jumped up for a closer look. The wall was packed with honey, with waxy combs of it, from floor to ceiling. "Whatever will you do with all this honey?"

"We'll sell it, of course," replied the practical Hulda, always calm in the face of every adversity. "I have plenty of empty jars in the pantry. The children can scoop it up. And John will just have to scrub the wall afterward, and seal it again."

"Oh, Ma," Irene objected. "I don't want to touch that sticky stuff."

"Well, you're going to. Everyone will have to help."

The honey-wall project took days. It seemed the more the children scooped with big soup spoons, the more honey oozed from the wall. John supervised, offering advice where it wasn't needed. After the honey finally was salvaged, John scrubbed and scrubbed and sealed and sealed. But the dining room wall never looked quite the same again.

Irene was a straight "A" student, but she felt she needed some extra study to prepare for the entrance exams coming up. She didn't want to take a chance of missing out on high school. Florence offered her services as tutor, thinking this was the least she could do in return for Irene's help. Without her, she never could have managed the Hendricks school. Studies were going well until one Saturday, when a rattle-trap of a truck pulled into the yard and a troop of children piled out. They looked like gypsies, dirty and dressed in peculiar clothing, and so did the parents who herded them toward the kitchen door.

"My God!" Florence said. "Who are all these people? I see seven children. Seven!"

Irene peered outside. "Oh, oh. That's my aunt Emmy and her lazy husband, Luke. I bet they've come to mooch on us for a while."

"But the house is bulging as it is. Whatever will we do?"

"Ma will find a way. She always does. I guess from now on, I'll have to do my studying at school. When Emmy and Luke come, they stay forever."

"I haven't seen my sister Emmy in years," Hulda explained to Florence later, looking as unruffled as ever. "I can put some of the children over to the neighbors. But this will mean a lot of cooking. It's going to be like feeding a threshing crew."

The next weeks brought nothing but turmoil. Makeshift beds and piles of suitcases littered the floor in the parlor. It was like an obstacle course for Florence to get to her bedroom, while Emmy did nothing to help restore order. According to Emmy's philosophy, if clothes didn't get washed, then they just didn't get washed. It wasn't unusual to find Emmy sitting in the midst of scuffling children and heaps of dirty laundry, absorbed in reading the Bible.

The story slowly came out about Luke, who had felt the call to be a lay preacher in Canada. He had sold his farm and all his worldly goods, and his lack of success in this venture reminded Florence of the Soudnes family back in North Dakota. Luke and Emma were just as destitute and lazy, but their faith was unshaken. They did nothing to help at the farm. Morning and evening milking duties always fell to John and Hulda. By the time the second week rolled around, Florence wondered how much longer her landlords could afford to support this indolent family. The provisions in the larder were disappearing as fast as Luke at chore time.

"Emmy, aren't you worried about the future?" Florence asked one day, coming home to the chaos. It had been another trying day at school and she sank into a chair in the cramped parlor. "What do you plan to do about finding a place to live? And about making a living?"

Emmy, clad in a hand-me-down dress from Hulda, was patching a skirt for one of her girls. "The Lord will provide, Miss Thompson. Consider the lillies of the field."

"I guess I read a different part of the Bible. About how man shall earn his living by the sweat of his brow."

Florence stepped over the profusion of suitcases and went to her room. She threw herself on the bed, feeling too unhappy and too exhausted, to even cry.

The visit from Emmy and Luke lasted for three weeks and Florence and Irene stayed at school to study. Finally, the tribe departed and when examination day came, John took Irene to the superintendent's office in Hendricks. She passed with no problem at all and probably could have done just as well without a tutor.

A letter arrived from Leonard with some exciting news. He had started a new job, helping to set up an automobile dealership for a rich man in Minot. They were going to sell a new model called Chrysler and if everything went as planned, he soon should be making enough money to get married. Leonard appeared to be riding on the wave of the future. It seemed he had found his niche in life at last.

Florence sailed through the end of the term, bade her fond farewells to the Waugh family, and John took her to Benson. Before she boarded the Great Northern for Minot, she paid a visit to Ida and Rudolph. She hadn't even seen the first baby and now Ida was expecting a second.

"How wonderful to see you," Ida said. "Now come in the kitchen. I want to show you something grand. Rudolph got it for me and it's the best present I ever had." She pointed to her kitchen ceiling, to a long cord that dangled from a socket next to a bare light bulb. She demonstrated how the cord could be attached to her new wringer washing machine, and how easily she could roll it in from the kitchen porch.

"You see," Ida continued. "We have electricity at last. This is just like living in the city."

"I wish you could come to the wedding," Florence said, properly awestruck by Ida's kitchen improvement. "Minot is so far away, I don't expect any of the family will be able to come. And Leonard can't get any time off from work. But we will be together at last. I was beginning to think this day would never come."

Florence swallowed back a lump in her throat. It was hard to say goodbye to Ida when she had no idea when she might see her again. Ida had stood by her like a true friend, in the best and in the worst of times.

"I'll miss you so much," she added. "I'll never forget how you saved me from smallpox. I'll never forget the wonderful weekends at your house, or those evening musicales with Rudolph playing the fiddle. Please write to me."

After their last farewell the next day, Florence boarded the train for another visit to the Cottingtons. Now she and Leonard could start looking for a furnished cottage to rent. Anything they could find would be heaven, after living out of a battered old trunk. There would be no more stingy school boards to deal with, no more boarding places, no more feeling like a stranger at the table.

And yet. . .she would miss the happy times, the opening day of school, the programs, the children. Florence settled back into her seat on the dusty train, letting her imagination wander into the future.

Would Leonard be waiting at the depot to meet her with an armful of flowers? Somehow, knowing the way he liked to surprise her, she was certain he would be.

Afterword

Florence and Leonard on their wedding day, August 1921

It would be fun to believe that Florence and Leonard were married in the summer of 1919 when this story ends, but that was not the case.

What had happened that summer to postpone the wedding once again? Was it the same old problem of not enough money? It's a bit of a mystery. School records reveal that Florence returned to North Dakota in September 1919 and was a teacher at the Washington School District 19, north of Scranton. That fact was unknown to me, when I was drafting my original outline. My mother never mentioned it.

The real wedding did not occur until August 2, 1921. The ceremony took place at the home of Norma and Ed Cottington in Minot without any relatives in attendance and during the time my father was working at the bank. The newly-weds moved into a little bungalow and soon afterward, Leonard experienced the break of a lifetime. A wealthy man named Clarence Holt asked him to set up a Chrysler dealership in Watertown, South Dakota. The imperious Mr. Holt became his close friend and mentor. Now Leonard, who some said would never amount to anything, was on his way to making his mark in the automobile business.

As the self-appointed family historian, I am filled with regret about not asking more questions when I had the chance. However, I can come up with one explanation for those missing years, which makes a little sense. While living in Watertown SD and believing they were unable to have children, my parents decided to adopt a baby. But no babies were available at the local orphanage, so they adopted a four-year-old boy, my brother Bob. In those days, people were not so open and honest about adoption and since Bob was older than their marriage, my mother thought she had to fabricate a different wedding date—1919. After my parents moved to Minneapolis in 1925, she began to tell that little white lie to cover up the truth about Bob. After a while, I think she started to believe it herself and just let those missing years slip from her memory.

Here is another strange twist to the story in Watertown. Doctors can be wrong with a diagnosis and this particular doctor was dead wrong. Three natural children were born in Minneapolis—Keith, Audrey (myself) and Jeanne. The truth has a way of coming out eventually, and when Bob had to produce a birth certificate when he was drafted into the army in 1941, I finally heard about the adoption. My father credited Bob's arrival in the family as the reason for such an unexpected turn of events. He was overjoyed when Keith was born and filled Mother's hospital room with flowers.

My father's career took off like a rocket in Minneapolis. He was promoted to Executive Vice-President of the newly established Holt Motor Company and bought a house. His widowed father, Lars, retired from farming and came to live with our family each winter. As young children, we made many trips to the farm, now passed down to Orin and his wife, Lillie. I have vivid recollections of kerosene lamps and an outdoor privy and what it was like to keep milk cold in a root cellar. Or attempt to. Rural electrification finally came to Six Mile Grove Township about 1937.

So what happened to the other people in the story? Ida and Rudolph Johnson lived in the same house in Benson for 45 years and raised a family of four children. Rudolph and his brother bought the hardware store and Rudolph some lake property where the Johnson family descendants still have reunions.

Grandmother Betsy Hanson, the matriarch of the clan, lived to a ripe old age and died in 1923. The bachelor sons, Bernt and Julius, surprised everyone by marrying sisters, and they established their own farms and families. The original house was passed down to the daughter, Caroline, who attempted to carry on with the help of her sons. This did not work out as the boys knew little about farming and did not speak Norwegian, still the prevailing language in the Sunburg area. Eventually, the house was sold and has undergone several renovations.

Bernice married a farmer in Bowman County, raised two children and played the piano for her church almost all her life. Wallace also homesteaded in Bowman County, married and raised a family. The brother, Tom, came home from the war after being gassed in the trenches, but he was never the same. He developed a problem with alcohol and committed suicide in 1929. Clara and Robert gave up homesteading and moved to Bowman around 1925, where they opened a restaurant. Robert served as sheriff for several years. After his death in 1948, Clara moved to southern California to be near the three daughters. She and Florence kept in close touch and arranged several Thompson family reunions.

Isabelle continued to grumble about how she was born "fifty years too soon" and seemed envious of her daughter, Florence, and her modern house in Minneapolis. My dad was always the first to get a new convenience, such as the latest model refrigerator or radio. Isabelle decided my father was not so bad after all, and she often came for visits. When her health started to fail, she moved to Benson and died there in 1941.

After several futile attempts to go on the stage, Irene Waugh married but never settled down. She embarked on a long career as an English and Drama teacher and often visited at our house. Irene provided the wonderful picture of Florence with John Waugh taken on Easter Day at his mother's farm in1919.

My father's career took another surprising turn in 1938, when he decided to open his own Chrysler dealership in Milwaukee, Wisconsin. He titled it Kvam Motor Company, although hardly anyone could pronounce the name. My mother was reluctant to leave Minneapolis but she packed us up as soon as school was out, and we drove to Milwaukee in her new Plymouth. Dad was active in civic and business affairs and won a host of friends who all called him "Mike"—a nickname he had picked up along the way. He attributed his success to my mother—"the best wife a man could ever want." In the midst of this move, our beloved grandfather died. Lars was buried at Six Mile Grove Church cemetery, the resting place of a long list of Kvam pioneers.

My parents loved to travel to exotic places and planned a trip at least once a year. In 1954, on their last trip together, they went to Norway. My dad could even remember a few words of the language. Mother wrote travelogues on all these adventures, larded with facts for our edification. As my father used to say when she was taking notes: "Once a schoolteacher, always a schoolteacher. It's in her bones." His untimely death at age 58, due to cancer, almost broke her heart. Just ten years before, she had suffered another blow, the loss of my brother, Keith. He had joined the 10th Mountain Division and was killed in action just before the end of World War II. Brother Bob survived the war and now lives in a retirement home in Atlanta, Georgia.

After my father's death and faced with years of widowhood, my mother found solace in spending time with my four small children. She invited them for weekends at her apartment in Milwaukee and to her retirement home in Florida. She was a profound influence on their lives and one reason why they never questioned the value of education. She read stories to them just as she had read to us as children, and encouraged them in every way. She was as proud as I was, when they graduated from college. Three went on to earn advanced degrees.

As the years passed, Florence kept up a vast correspondence with all the relatives. She was generous with everyone, including two nephews that she and my dad put through college. She stayed fiercely independent almost to the end. Since she refused to come to live with me, I moved to Sarasota to be nearby. We had some good times together, going to dinner shows and concerts during her declining years. It was a sad day when we lost her at the age of 93. At her request, she is buried next to my dad and Keith in Milwaukee, the city where she had spent her happiest years.

Florence

References

The Moorhead Normal School; Clarence A. Glasrun; published 1987 under a grant from the Moorhead State University Alumni Association.

Swift County Minnesota, published 1979 by the Swift County Historical Society. A collection of historical sketches, family histories and pictures.

Diamond Jubilee History of Rhame published 1983 by the Bowman County Pioneer, Rhame ND 58651. A collection of historical sketches and pictures.

The Benson Museum, Benson, Minnesota 56215; provided newspaper clippings.